Steve Parish

Amazing Facts about Australian
Mammals

Text: Greg Czechura, Queensland Museum

Photography: Steve Parish

AMAZING FACTS — AUSTRALIAN MAMMALS

Contents

Australia's
amazing mammals

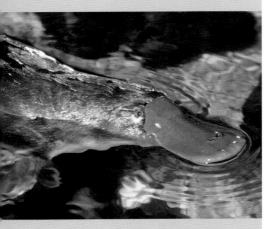

Above: Numbats are termite eaters.

Above: Platypus *Below:* Short-beaked Echidna. These are both egg-laying mammals or monotremes.

The first Europeans to reach Australian shores were startled and perplexed by the peculiar creatures they found. Animals they were familiar with were missing. In their place was a unique assembly of some of the most intriguing mammals ever discovered on Earth and all were superbly adapted to their life in the "Great Southern Land".

MOST AUSTRALIAN MAMMALS can trace their origins back to the ancient supercontinent of Gondwana, but their evolution has been shaped by millions of years of isolation. Around 45 million years ago, the Australia–New Guinea landmass separated from the rest of Gondwana. The massive environmental and climatic changes set in motion by this upheaval meant all the animals simply had to adapt, or perish.

Some of the mammals that scurried around the warm, wet rainforests of 60 million years ago died out, but many others thrived in their new environment. These animals learned to live in a harsh and sometimes hostile landscape. As Australia became browner and drier, they developed unique characteristics that, even today, set them apart from the rest of the world.

The first people reached Australia's shores around 50,000–60,000 years ago and European settlers a mere 200 years ago. Although humans came to Australia relatively recently, in that time they have fundamentally altered the natural environment and pose continuing threats and challenges to its animals.

This book looks at Australia's native mammals and their special place in this country known as the "wide brown land".

ABOUT THIS BOOK

As you progress through the pages that follow, you will be amazed at the diversity of mammalian fauna in Australia. There is logic to the order in which this diversity has been presented. Each section consists of a body of text in which the main story about mammals in Australia unfolds and informs.

Supporting this text on each page is a side panel of short facts. Use this panel as a "quick reference" to truly amazing snippets provided in easy-to-read bites.

In the top right-hand panel on many pages you will find a "Conservation Watch" section. These panels give an indication of the conservation status of the species and some of the threats affecting that species' survival. It is an unfortunate fact that Australia has one of the worst records in the world for mammalian extinctions.

We need be ever mindful that many of our native animals live on a finely balanced knife edge between existence and extinction. Australian ecosystems may be harsh but they are also easily disrupted, and even small changes can bring about disastrous consequences for flora and fauna.

The main text discusses mammals in taxonomic order (closely related animals are grouped together). This will assist you to easily locate a particular mammal or group of mammals.

The information in these pages contains truly amazing facts about Australia's unique and beautiful mammals in all their incredible and precious diversity.

Below: Sleek Australian Sea-lions cavorting beneath the waves.

RON & VALERIE TAYLOR

the FACTS!

AUSTRALIA HAS ABOUT 360 SPECIES of living native mammals, from tiny marsupial mice to the Red Kangaroo, which can stand taller than a man. Humans have introduced another 23 species, including dogs, cats, rabbits, sheep, goats, cows, camels and horses.

EARLY EXPLORERS and naturalists found it difficult to describe Australian mammals to a European audience. They often had to portray an Australian mammal as being made up of parts from more familiar animals. For example, small wallabies were likened to two-legged civets or cats with the paws and tails of monkeys.

THE FIRST ACCOUNT OF AUSTRALIAN MAMMALS was written by English buccaneer William Dampier, who landed on the coast of Western Australia in 1688. Dampier described the hare-wallabies he saw as a "sort of Raccoon". He also said they were "very good meat".

THE KANGAROO is one of Australia's best known animals and a national icon. It appears on the Australian coat of arms and other state and territory emblems. A red kangaroo is the symbol for Australia's national airline, Qantas.

What is
a mammal?

the FACTS!

MAMMALS, LIKE BIRDS, GENERATE HEAT within their bodies, rather than absorbing it from their surroundings, to "power" their lives. Animals that have the ability to do this are known as "homeotherms".

THE SMALLEST AUSTRALIAN MAMMALS are the Northern Cave Bat (*Vespadelus caurinus*) and the Long-tailed Planigale (*Planigale ingrami*). These animals weigh less than 5 g each and have a head–body length of less than 6 mm.

THE MOST COMMON FORM of mammal shape is a rat-like body.

MAMMALS HAVE A SOPHISTICATED HEARING SYSTEM consisting of three middle-ear bones (the malleus, incus and stapes). Other vertebrates have these bones, but their only function is to link the lower jaw to the skull.

AUSTRALIA'S LARGEST LIVING NATIVE LAND MAMMAL is the male Red Kangaroo (below), which can weigh up to 85 kg and measure 2.5 m from nose to tail.

Humans have a special affinity with mammals, and for good reason. Most of the animals we depend on as our food, such as cows and sheep, are mammals, as are the pets that keep us company. Perhaps the simplest reason for our special connection to mammals is that we humans are mammals too.

MAMMALS ARE A SPECTACULAR AND DIVERSE GROUP that range in size from one of the largest animals that has ever lived — the 30 m long Blue Whale — to the tiny 30 mm Bumblebee Bat of South-East Asia. Along with fish, amphibians, reptiles and birds, mammals are vertebrates — animals with an internal skeleton and backbone.

Mammals differ from other vertebrates because their body is covered by skin and hair. Even "naked" mammals have a few hairs somewhere on their bodies. Another difference is that their young suckle milk produced by glands on the mother's body. Mammals also have lower jaws that hinge directly to their skulls and their teeth vary in shape.

A BASIC PLAN

Mammals all have the same basic body plan — a head and neck and a long body with four limbs that each end in five digits (fingers and toes). Some also have a tail. Their internal skeleton provides a light-weight, rigid framework to support the body and a series of flexible joints permits easy movement. This basic layout has been modified and altered to suit particular lifestyles. For example, the limbs can be modified to act as wings, flippers, hooves or hands. The nostrils of whales and dolphins are located on the top of the head to form their characteristic "blowholes", rather than in the middle of the face.

IAN MORRIS

Above: Bats are the only mammal species that can fly.

JAWS AND TEETH

Mammals have four types of teeth: incisors (front teeth) for biting and gnawing; canines (eye teeth) for ripping and tearing; and premolars and molars (cheek teeth) for crushing or shearing. The arrangement and number of teeth in the jaws varies according to diet. Numbats (termite eaters) have 52 teeth!

Australia's marsupial mammals can be divided into two groups, according to the number of their incisors. Koalas, wombats, possums and kangaroos have two lower incisors and are known as *diprotodonts*, meaning two front teeth (right top). Carnivorous marsupials — bandicoots, marsupial moles and Numbats — have more than two lower incisors and are known as *polyprotodonts*, meaning many front teeth (right bottom).

QM-GC

Above: Desert environment.

Above: Grassland environment.

Above: Forest and woodland environment.

Above: Aquatic and marine environment.

WHERE DO MAMMALS LIVE?

Australian mammals live in the oceans, on wide grassy plains, in lush forests and harsh deserts and on the highest mountains.

DESERT MAMMALS

Deserts are harsh environments with extreme temperatures and little or no water. Mammals have to find ways of coping with the heat and conserving moisture. Most mammals are active at night and hide in burrows, or shelter in crevices under rocks and grass tussocks during the day.

GRASSLAND MAMMALS

Grasslands are open, usually treeless, spaces in drier regions, or where the soil is poor or shallow. Mammals are common in grasslands and large herds of grazing animals are a feature of these habitats around the world.

FOREST AND WOODLAND MAMMALS

Forests and woodlands differ in number and types of trees. Rainforests have a dense growth of very tall trees. Woodlands are more open with fewer trees and usually a layer of low-growing shrubs or grass as groundcover. Trees provide mammals with food, shelter, safety and nest sites.

AQUATIC AND MARINE MAMMALS

Life in the water calls for special adaptations. Mammals with semi-aquatic life cycles usually have dense waterproof fur, webbed feet and flattened or paddle-shaped tails. Marine mammals that live permanently in water tend to have smooth, streamlined bodies; flippers and fins instead of limbs; flat fish-like tails; and a thick layer of fat to keep them warm.

Right: Squirrel Glider in a nest hollow.

the FACTS!

GRASSLANDS MAY LOOK SIMILAR, but they support different animal populations, depending on what types of grasses grow there. Areas with diverse plant species are likely to have more types of animals than an area dominated by a single type of grass.

AUSTRALIA WAS ONCE ALMOST COMPLETELY COVERED in rainforests, but has been slowly drying out for hundreds of millions of years.

THE NUMBER AND ARRANGEMENT of mammal teeth are influenced by diet. Carnivores have sharp, conical teeth, with long and prominent canines. Herbivores have large, flat premolars, molars for grinding plants, and small or non-existent canine teeth.

TREE HOLLOWS PROVIDE SHELTERS for many smaller forest and woodland mammals, but larger animals often rely on colour and body shape to camouflage them among the leaves and branches.

Identifying mammals
— their own special place

Above: The Delicate Mouse (right) and Eastern Pebble-mound Mouse (left) were once thought to be the same species.

the FACTS!

THE SCIENCE OF CLASSIFYING (describing and naming) plants and animals is called "taxonomy".

EVEN IN TODAY'S MODERN WORLD new mammals are still being discovered — and not always in remote places. The Cypriot Mouse (*Mus cypriacus*) was discovered on the heavily populated island of Cyprus in the Mediterranean in 2006. A bizarre rodent from Laos, *Laonastes aenigmamus*, discovered in 2005, was familiar to local people, but had never been identified by scientists. The most recently described Australian mammal is the Australian Snubfin Dolphin (*Orcaella heinsohni*). It was described as a new species in 2005. It is possible there are more species of mammals yet to be discovered in Australia, but on land they are most likely to be small and in remote habitats.

UNRELATED ANIMALS that have similar lifestyles often look similar, even though they are not closely related. This is called *convergent evolution*. For example, the marsupial moles of Australia look almost identical to the golden moles of southern Africa.

IN THE PAST, there were many more types of mammals and many of these groups have no living representatives. Fossil species can also be classified and named using the Linnean system.

Naming and identifying things is fundamental to how humans make sense of the world around them. For example, mammals come in many shapes and forms — a whale is different from a rat and there are different types of whales and rats. The process of naming and identifying things is called "classification".

SCIENTISTS USE A SYSTEM OF CLASSIFICATION that is recognised around the world to study and describe the natural environment. The Linnean system was developed by 18th-century Swedish botanist Carolus Linnaeus and it gives each plant or animal its own place in the natural world. As part of this process, each living thing is also given a scientific name that identifies its genus and species. This Latin-based name is recognised by scientists around the world and defines an animal's relationship to others of its type.

Above: Scientific specimens are used to obtain information about animals. They are used to describe variations in a species and find differences between similar species such as these "wrist-winged" glider skins: Mahogany Glider (top), Squirrel Glider (middle), Sugar Glider.

HOW MANY MAMMALS?

There are more than 5000 species of living mammals belonging to more than 1000 genera, 140 families, 20 orders and two subclasses. The most numerous groups of living mammals are the rodents, with 2000 species, followed by bats, with 1000 species, then insectivores (365 species), primates (360 species), marsupials (290 species), carnivores (231 species) and hoofed mammals (220 species). All other mammals are represented by less than 100 species and some only by a single species.

Right: Eastern Pygmy-possums live on insects and flowers.

MAMMALS CAN BE DIVIDED INTO THREE GROUPS, depending on how they reproduce. One group lay eggs like reptiles. The second group give birth to "premature" young that continue to develop on the outside of the mother's body, usually in a pouch. The young of the remaining group develop inside their mother's body.

MONOTREMES

The young develop in soft-shelled eggs nourished by yolk. These eggs are incubated outside the mother's body for a short time. Hatchlings are blind, naked and undeveloped. They suckle milk from the mother, but female monotremes do not have nipples on their mammary glands. Instead, the milk drains from the gland onto a patch of skin or tufts of hair. Young echidnas are cared for in a pouch, but young Platypuses develop in a nest after they hatch. Monotremes have a single opening (cloaca), for mating and passing body wastes. Monotreme means "single hole".

MARSUPIALS

Marsupials give birth to partly developed young after a short gestation period. The newborn "swims" through its mother's fur to locate a teat. In most marsupials, the mammary gland and teat are located in a pouch or a fold of skin on the mother's abdomen. The young complete their development on the outside of their mother. Marsupials also have a single reproductive and excretory opening.

PLACENTALS

Most mammals develop inside the mother in a muscular organ called the uterus. The embryo is nourished directly from the mother's system through the placenta, which links the blood vessels of the mother to her baby and prevents it from being rejected by her body. Some placental young are born blind and naked; others as small, fully formed versions of their parents. All suckle from their mothers until they can fend for themselves. Placentals have separate openings for defecation (anus) and reproduction or urine excretion (urinogenital opening).

TO WHICH GROUP DO AUSTRALIAN NATIVE MAMMALS BELONG?

MONOTREMES	MARSUPIALS	PLACENTALS
Platypus	Quoll, dunnart and relatives	Bat
Echidna	Thylacine and Tasmanian Devil	Rodent
	Numbat	Seal and sea-lion
	marsupial mole	Whale and dolphin
	Bandicoot and Bilby	Dugong
	Wombat and Koala	
	Possum and glider	
	Kangaroo and wallaby	

the FACTS!

MAMMALS ARE DESCENDED from mammal-like reptiles that lived 210–280 million years ago.

THE EARLIEST MAMMAL FOSSILS date from around 220 million years ago (Triassic Period).

ALL THREE GROUPS of modern mammals evolved during the time of the dinosaurs.

FOSSIL AND GENETIC EVIDENCE shows that monotremes separated from the line of mammals that gave rise to marsupials and placental animals about 150 million years ago.

MARSUPIALS AND PLACENTAL mammals seem to have parted company sometime between 100 million and 125 million years ago.

THE RISE AND DOMINANCE of the dinosaurs seems to have restricted the development of mammals during the Mesozoic Period but, with the demise of the dinosaurs, the "Age of Mammals" began and continues to this day.

The age
of mammals

Above: Gondwana 95–98 million years ago.

the FACTS!

A FOSSIL IS THE REMAINS or traces of a plant or animal that lived in the past.

IMPORTANT FOSSIL MAMMAL SITES in Australia are: Tingamurra, Riversleigh and the Darling Downs in Queensland; Alcoota in the Northern Territory; Naracoorte in South Australia; Wellington Caves in New South Wales; Dinosaur Cove in Victoria; and the Devil's Lair and caves of the Nullarbor in Western Australia.

ALTHOUGH THE EARLIEST FOSSILS of marsupials have all been found in North America, the remains of a small marsupial-like animal, dating to 125 million years ago, have been discovered in China.

THE DISCOVERY OF THE RIVERSLEIGH fossil field in north-west Queensland has changed our understanding of the development of Australia's mammals. The remains of thousands of prehistoric mammals have been found at the site, including kangaroos, bandicoots, wombats, thylacines, dasyurids, Koalas, possums, cuscuses, bats, rodents and Platypuses. The Riversleigh field contains hundreds of individual sites dating from about 15 million to 25 million years ago and includes many other groups of animals as well.

Australia and New Guinea are the only places in the world where living monotremes, marsupials and placentals coexist. Two families of marsupials (the opossums and shrew opossums) occur in the Americas, but other countries only have placental mammals.

THE HISTORY OF MAMMALS AND THEIR EVOLUTION is an ancient one. Mammals are descended from mammal-like reptiles that lived some 210–280 million years ago. The oldest mammal fossils date from around 220 million years ago (Triassic Period), but all major mammal groups had evolved before the end of the Mesozoic Period (250–265 million years ago).

Fossil and other evidence shows that monotremes were already distinct from other mammals around 150 million years ago. Marsupials and placentals seem to have parted company sometime before 100 million years ago.

Above: The largest Australian mammal of all time was *Diprotodon opatum*. It was also the first fossil mammal from Australia to be described.

GONDWANA ORIGINS

The ancestors of most Australian plants and animals inhabited the great southern supercontinent of Gondwana. This ancient landmass started breaking up around 180 million years ago and gave rise to the smaller continents of India, South America, Africa, Australia and Antarctica, as well as the islands of New Guinea and Madagascar.

The separation of Australia and New Guinea from Antarctica about 45 million years ago was the final act in a long geological process that spanned some 140 million years. The evolution of Australia's mammals was shaped by the fate of Gondwana. Australia's isolation resulted in the emergence of its unique fauna.

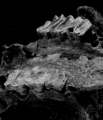

LEFT: QM. CENTRE & RIGHT: QM·GC

THE EARLIEST INHABITANTS

The oldest Australian mammal fossils date from the time when Australia was still part of Gondwana. The early Gondwanan mammals were mainly monotremes and their close relatives. There was also a mysterious group, the ausktribosphenids, present during the Early Cretaceous Period (135–197 million years ago).

It is likely that the first marsupials arrived in Australia before the extinction of the dinosaurs (65 million years ago). Marsupials originated in North America and reached Australia by way of South America and Antarctica. The earliest Australian marsupial fossils date to 55 million years ago.

Left: The Platypus-like monotreme *Steropodon* lived alongside the dinosaurs. It is one of the earliest known Australian mammals.

THE RISE OF THE MARSUPIALS AND FIRST PLACENTALS

Marsupials became the dominant group of Australian mammals during the Eocene Era (about 53–34 million years ago) as the continent became fully separated from Antarctica.

The period of greatest marsupial diversity occurred during the Miocene Period (23–5.3 million years ago), when wet rainforests covered most of the continent.

The first placental mammals to arrive in Australia were bats, around 55 million years ago. They were followed by marine mammals 28–23 million years ago and rodents around 4 million years ago.

Australia has become progressively drier and browner in the past five million years. Forest animals have declined, while grassland animals such as kangaroos and wombats have thrived.

Right: Living macropods are browsers and grazers. However, some extinct macropods, such as *Propleopus*, were partly carnivorous and dined on other animals when the opportunity arose.

MONOTREMES   MARSUPIALS   PLACENTALS

Present
QUARTERNARY
Tasmania cut off
Humans arrive; megafauna become extinct

2 million years ago

TERTIARY
Australia's mammal species respond to more arid climatic conditions
Australia separates from Antarctica and begins to drift northward
Decline of rainforest mammals

65 million years ago

CRETACEOUS
Dinosaurs and flying reptiles become extinct
Oldest Australian fossil mammals
Marsupials and placental animals diverge

145 million years ago

JURASSIC
Reptiles, including dinosaurs and flying pterosaurs, dominate the Earth
First birds appear
Monotremes diverge from other mammals

208 million years ago

TRIASSIC
Earliest mammals appear
Reptiles, including dinosaurs, dominate the land
Mammal-like reptiles appear

245 million years ago

PERMIAN
Amphibians decline in numbers
Reptiles become more abundant

AUSTRALIA'S MEGAFAUNA

When woolly mammoths and sabre-toothed big cats were roaming Europe, some very unique animals lived in Australia. This was the era of the giant mammals known as megafauna. Although they were smaller than dinosaurs, the largest megafauna dwarfed the biggest domestic horses and cattle and each continent had its own very special set of mammal giants.

Large mammals started appearing throughout the world from about 5 million years ago. Suddenly, mass extinctions of these giants occurred from 68,000 to 35,000 years ago. Possible causes of these extinctions include climate change, disease, ecological factors (such as fire), human exploitation or a combination of all these.

The Australian megafauna was dominated by giant wombats and kangaroos. The largest of all was *Diprotodon opatum*, which was related to wombats and reached up to 3 m in length and 2.6 m in height. There were also giant kangaroos such as *Procoptodon*, *Sthenurus* and *Protemnodon*; the so-called marsupial tapir, *Palorchestes azael*; and the marsupial lion, *Thylacaleo carnifex*, with its shear-like teeth and partly opposable thumbs. There were even giant monotremes, such as the echidna, *Zaglossus hacketti*, which weighed around 30 kg.

Left: The skull structure of the so-called marsupial tapirs (*Palorchestes* species) indicates that they possessed a short tapir-like trunk and a long, thin tongue like that of a giraffe.

the FACTS!

SO FAR, SCIENTISTS have described around 400 species of fossil mammals from Australia. Many more are still to be studied.

AUSTRALIA'S MEGAFAUNA were dwarfed by those of other continents. The largest, *Diprotodon*, only grew to the size of a small van or a rhinoceros.

THE FIRST COMPLETE SKELETON of *Thylacoleo carnifex*, the "marsupial lion", was discovered along with giant wombats and kangaroos in 2006 in a cave 20–70 metres under the Nullarbor Plain.

CAVES AND DESERTS hold many fossils. Often it is cave explorers who discover fossilised bones in limestone caverns, like at Naracoorte. The Fossil Chamber contains animals that fell in and died there thousands of years ago.

DISAPPEARANCE OF THE MEGAFAUNA

Their enormous size indicates that the largest megafauna would have been long-lived and slow to mature. This made them more vulnerable to severe environmental change, competition, disease epidemics or excessive predation. The wave of extinction that passed through the world's megafaunas left few survivors.

Recent fossil discoveries in caves on the Nullarbor Plain indicate that this area was once home to 23 species of kangaroos and wallabies, including tree-kangaroos, giant wombats, thylacines and *Thylacoleo carnifex*. The extinction of most of these animals seems to have been caused by a sudden vegetation change from woodland to almost treeless grassland due to fire. It is unknown if the fires were due to natural events or humans.

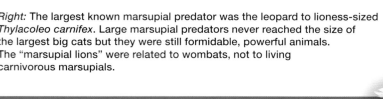

Right: The largest known marsupial predator was the leopard to lioness-sized *Thylacoleo carnifex*. Large marsupial predators never reached the size of the largest big cats but they were still formidable, powerful animals. The "marsupial lions" were related to wombats, not to living carnivorous marsupials.

Conservation Watch

Brumbies and feral goats eat the food of native animals and trample the habitat. Foxes prey on many small native animals.

THE INVADERS

The first humans reached Australia about 50,000–60,000 years ago. It is possible that their hunting and burning practices may have caused the extinction of megafauna animals, which died out 35,000–40,000 years ago. The later introduction of the Dingo, around 4000 years ago, almost certainly resulted in the disappearance of the Thylacine (Tasmanian Tiger) from mainland Australia.

European settlers arrived a mere 200 years ago, bringing a host of exotic placental mammals with them. Many pets and livestock were deliberately introduced, but some, such as mice and rats, came as stowaways in cargo. Early European settlers also attempted to "remodel" Australia into a more familiar setting by introducing familiar plants and animals.

These exotic animals thrived in the Australian environment and became "feral". They preyed on native animals or caused extensive damage to habitats through grazing or their behaviour. The European Rabbit, for example, was introduced into south-eastern Australia in 1859 and within a mere 60 years colonised much of the continent, outcompeting native species for food and burrows.

Since European settlement, at least 19 native species have become extinct, while another 9 survive only on offshore islands that are free of introduced predators and competitors.

Above: Dingo (*Canis lupus dingo*).

Above: European Rabbit (*Oryctolagus cuniculus*).

Above: Wild Pig (*Sus scrofa*).

Above: Ferret (*Mustella furo*).

Above: House Cat (*Felix catus*).

the FACTS!

MEGAFAUNA KANGAROOS were not only grazing herbivores. Some extinct species were omnivores and others were carnivores. The largest, such as *Propleopus*, were the size of living kangaroos.

THE THEORY THAT HUNTING caused the megafauna extinctions is also known as the "blitzkrieg theory".

AUSTRALIA'S MAMMALS include about 360 indigenous and 23 exotic species. It is likely that new species will be identified in the future and, sadly, that the list of feral species will increase.

THE FERRET appears to have recently become established in Tasmania, making it the most recent addition to Australia's list of pest mammals.

FERAL STOATS, weasels, ferrets and mink pose grave threats to wildlife around the world — even to others of their kind.

FERAL RABBIT POPULATIONS have declined in recent years while camels are increasing in numbers and foxes are becoming more widespread.

THE FOX POPULATION in Australia is estimated at 7.2 million and these animals consume about 190 million birds every year.

THE FERAL PIG population is estimated at about 23 million in Australia. The pigs destroy the vegetation that protects against erosion. Uneroded soil keeps vegetation intact that provides food and nesting sites for native wildlife.

AUSTRALIA has an estimated 2.6 million feral goats.

Improbable
Platypus

Order: Monotremata
Meaning: *mono* — single; *trema* — hole

In 1799, a cask containing the preserved remains of "a strange creature, half bird, half beast" arrived in England. The mystery animal, dubbed an "amphibious mole", amazed early naturalists. Many of them refused to believe it was a real animal and dismissed it as a hoax or prank.

the FACTS!

THE PLATYPUS AND THE ECHIDNA are the world's only living monotremes. The earliest Australian monotremes were Platypus-like animals that lived during the Early Cretaceous Period about 105 million years ago.

AN AVERAGE MALE Platypus is 50 cm long and weighs 1.7 kg. Females are smaller at about 43 cm in length and 0.9 kg in weight.

MALE PLATYPUSES have a poisonous spur on the inner side of each hind limb (below). The spurs, which can inflict a painful wound, are used to fight other males and as a defence against predators. Each spur is connected via a hollow duct to a poison gland in the animal's body.

DAVE WATTS/ANT PHOTO

THE HEALTH OF A PLATYPUS is indicated by the condition of its tail, which is used to store fat — the fatter the tail, the healthier the Platypus.

PLATYPUSES CAN VOCALISE and make growling sounds if disturbed or threatened.

THE ANIMAL WAS A PLATYPUS (*Ornithorhynchus anatinus*), one of Australia's greatest natural treasures. The Platypus has sometimes been described as a "furred reptile" or "primitive mammal" because it lays eggs like a reptile, but suckles its young like a mammal.

Above: Most aquatic mammals swim by kicking their back feet. The Platypus, however, uses its front feet.

Above: On dry land, Platypuses walk on their knuckles to protect the webbing of their front feet. The webbing is folded over the soles of the feet.

LIFE IN THE WATER

The Platypus, with its streamlined body, is superbly adapted for a semi-aquatic life. It is a strong swimmer, but moves slowly using alternate strokes of the front feet, which have very large webs. The hindfeet are also webbed, but are used mainly for steering and braking. The flat paddle-shaped tail acts like a rudder.

Underwater, a Platypus closes its eyes, ears and nostrils and relies on its sensitive bill to find food and develop a "map" of its surroundings.

The bill has many tactile sensors to detect movement produced by Platypus prey in the water.

Conservation Watch

Platypuses are common, but seldom seen, inhabitants of freshwater streams, rivers, lakes and lagoons of eastern Australia. However, habitat loss, the construction of dams, pollution and feral predators all threaten their existence.

SECRET BURROWS

When not searching for food, Platypuses shelter in burrows excavated along the banks of waterways.

Platypuses build two types of burrows — "nesting burrows", which shelter mother and young, and "camping burrows". Both have a main chamber connected to a tunnel in the bank. Burrow entrances are located near the waterline and are usually hidden by vegetation or overhanging banks.

Adult Platypuses make several camping burrows and use different ones over a few weeks. No matter how far a Platypus swims, it is always close to a safe refuge. Platypuses sometimes share burrows, but adult animals tend to be solitary.

Radio-tagged Platypuses have occasionally been found sleeping inside hollow logs at the water's edge or in piles of branches and leaves trapped in the stream.

Above: In southern parts of Australia, Platypuses will hibernate in their burrows during cold winters.

the FACTS!

PLATYPUSES BREED from July to November and sometimes earlier in northern Australia. After an elaborate courtship that may last several days, the female lays one to three eggs in a deep nesting burrow lined with damp plant material. The eggs contain a partly developed embryo when laid and are about 17 mm long with a sticky coating. The female incubates them for 10–12 days by holding them between her belly and tail.

DR TOM GRANT

YOUNG PLATYPUSES feed on milk that oozes from ducts on the female's abdomen. Scientists believe the hairs around these ducts act like teats, enabling the young to suckle. It takes about six weeks for the young to open their eyes and become fully furred.

PLATYPUSES MATURE at two years of age and live for around 12 years. Males take no part in the care of the young.

THE WIDE LEATHERY BILL of the Platypus is equipped with thousands of tiny "sensors". Some sensors react to touch and others detect electrical impulses generated by prey animals.

ABORIGINAL AUSTRALIANS and European colonists prized Platypus fur and the animal was hunted until the early 20th century.

DAWN AND DUSK ARE FAVOURITE FORAGING TIMES for Platypuses, but they can occasionally be seen during the day, especially if conditions are overcast.

A Platypus spends around 12–13 hours of every day looking for food. It will remain submerged for 20–40 seconds, resting on the surface for 10 seconds between dives and can make about 80 dives every hour.

Platypuses feed on crayfish, insect larvae, snails, worms, tadpoles and fish. They consume about a quarter to half their own body weight each day.

When submerged, a Platypus sweeps its bill from side to side to locate food. Prey is stored in cheek-pouches and then carried to the surface to be eaten. Instead of teeth, Platypuses have small, horny pads on their upper and lower jaws for holding and crushing prey. Young Platypuses are born with teeth, but lose them when they are weaned at about 4–5 months.

Above: Platypuses have a dense luxuriant fur with more than 600 hairs per square millimetre. The waterproof outer fur keeps the animal dry and the woolly insulating underfur helps it to stay warm.

Echidnas
— short and sharp

Order: Monotremata
Meaning: *mono* — single; *trema* — hole

The Short-beaked Echidna (Tachyglossus aculeatus) *is the only species of native mammal that ranges across Australia. Echidnas are often called "spiny anteaters" because of their appearance and diet.*

LIKE THE PLATYPUS, the echidna is a monotreme — an egg-laying mammal. Echidnas have a long, tubular snout, coarse fur interspersed with yellowish spines and a short spiky tail. Fur colour varies from reddish-brown to black, depending on where the animal is found. In northern Australia, echidnas tend to be lighter, but in Tasmania echidnas are dark to almost black and they look less spiny than their mainland cousins because their fur is longer.

The echidna's short, powerful legs are tipped with long claws ideally suited to digging. Each hind foot has a very long claw that allows an echidna to scratch and groom between its spines.

Its snout is equipped with many sensors that help detect ants and termites.

Above: The echidna's hollow spines are actually modified hairs that are stiffened and lengthened to act as defensive weapons.

the FACTS!

AN ECHIDNA'S SNOUT is 7–8 cm long. Its small mouth and nostrils are located at the very tip. By contrast, its tongue is roughly twice as long (about 15–18 cm). Echidnas have an excellent sense of smell and this helps them to locate ant and termite nests.

THE SHORT-BEAKED ECHIDNA is also found in New Guinea, along with three types of long-beaked echidnas (*Zaglossus* species). Long-beaked echidnas are larger than their Australian cousins and their snouts are long and curved. They also have shorter hair and live mainly in high mountain forests.

AN ECHIDNA CAN LIFT objects twice its own weight.

ANOTHER NAME for an ant or termite-eating mammal is *myrmecophage* from *myrmeco* — "ants" and *phage* — "to eat".

LOVESICK MALES queue up behind a female, nose to tail, forming long trains. There can be up to 11 males at a time following along behind.

SOLITARY RAMBLERS

Echidnas are found in almost all habitats, but they are less common in desert areas. They tend to be solitary animals, roaming freely across their home territory, which, depending on the type and quality of habitat, ranges from 20 to almost 200 ha.

Echidnas do not build nests, but shelter in any available cover such as bushes, hollow logs or the burrows of other animals. Females dig a shallow burrow when incubating eggs or caring for their young.

Below: If disturbed or threatened, an echidna will usually lower its head and dig rapidly into the ground, leaving only its spines exposed. On hard surfaces, echidnas curl into balls (left) and they can also use their spines and legs to wedge themselves tightly into hollows or crevices.

A TASTE FOR ANTS

Echidnas eat mainly ants and termites, but they will also take insect larvae and worms. Large grubs are squashed, so the echidna can lick up the juices. When feeding, echidnas also swallow a lot of soil and ant-nest material, which is excreted in their droppings.

Mammals that specialise in eating ants and termites rely on the aggressive defense behaviour of these insects as a way to get a meal. An echidna will use its long sharp claws to rip open an ant nest, pushing its snout into the damaged area. As the ants swarm to attack, the echidna simply flicks its long, flexible tongue over the teeming insects catching them in its sticky saliva. In this way, an echidna is able to consume hundreds of ants or termites at a time.

A PUGGLE IN THE POUCH

Echidnas mate in late winter from about July to August, depending on climate. During the breeding season, the female develops a simple pouch and lays a single, soft-shelled egg about two weeks after mating.

A young echidna, called a "puggle", takes about 10 days to hatch and, like the Platypus, suckles milk secreted from its mother's body. Echidnas are born smooth and hairless and develop their spines at about three months. The young animal stays with the female for up to eight months after it leaves the pouch.

Adult male echidnas grow to about 30 cm long and weigh up to 7 kg. Females are a similar size, but are not as heavy.

The male echidna has a spur on its hind foot but, unlike the spur on a Platypus, it is not poisonous.

Echidnas are not related to the porcupines, hedgehogs or anteaters found in other parts of the world.

the FACTS!

IN THE WILD, echidnas live about 10–15 years, but the longest record for a captive animal is 50 years.

ECHIDNAS ARE INFESTED with what is said to be the world's largest flea: *Bradiopsylla echidnae*, which is about 4 mm long.

ECHIDNAS HAVE A LOWER BODY TEMPERATURE (about 31–32°C), than other mammals and in cooler climates may hibernate through the winter.

ALTHOUGH THEY ARE MOST AT HOME on solid ground, echidnas sometimes go to water to drink and are good swimmers. They paddle through the water with only the snout and a few spines showing. Echidnas have been seen crossing wide beaches to swim and groom themselves in the sea. The seawater may help to remove parasites that live in their fur.

DIFFERENT ABORIGINAL GROUPS hunted echidna and Platypus for food. Echidnas are slow-moving and could easily be caught.

Above: Adult and young echidnas lack teeth, so they grind their meal between the hard roof of the mouth and a series of ridges on the back of the tongue.

Carnivorous
mammals

Order: Dasyuromorphia
Meaning: *dasy* — hairy; *oura* — tail; *morphe* — form (forms of hairy-tails)

Australia's carnivorous land mammals have always been small by world standards. Most are tiny marsupials that belong to a group of animals known as dasyurids.

DASYURID MEANS "HAIRY-TAILED" and refers to the hairs or hairy crests along their tails. The largest living species is the Tasmanian Devil (*Sarcophilus harrisii*), which is the size of a small, stocky dog. The rest are cat-, rat- or mouse-sized creatures that are often wrongly called "native mice".

One way to tell dasyurids apart from rodents, such as rats and mice, is by their very pointed faces and jaws full of sharp teeth. Rodents have two chisel-like incisors on their upper and lower jaws with a gap between the incisors and their chewing molars.

Above: Their tiny size, pointed flattened heads and lithe bodies allow small dasyurids to squeeze through crevices with ease and to move almost unnoticed in leaf litter.

the FACTS!

A SMALL DASYURID will immobilise a larger spider by attacking it repeatedly and biting off its legs.

THE LONG-TAILED DUNNART (*Sminthopsis longicaudata*) has the longest tail of any small marsupial (below). Its tail is usually twice as long as its head and body and can be up to 20 cm in length. It is a nocturnal animal. The dunnart that inhabits the Gibson Desert of Central Australia uses its tail as a balance as it runs over rocks.

HAIRY-FOOTED DUNNARTS (*Sminthopsis hirtipes*), which live on the sand dunes of the Central Australian deserts, have fine silvery bristles covering the soles of their broad feet to help them move over loose sand.

SMALL DASYURIDS lose heat quickly because of their size, so they will often bask in the early morning sunshine or on warm rocks, to help conserve body heat.

FIERCE PREDATORS

Despite their small size and "cute" appearance, dasyurids are surprisingly savage nocturnal predators. They are very quick and agile and will attack and kill any animal they can overpower. They have been known to eat their young and also each other!

Prey animals are struck repeatedly with rapid bites to the head and body. Small dasyurids eat spiders, scorpions, centipedes, insects, reptiles and frogs, as well as small birds and mammals. Larger species eat reptiles, birds and mammals and occasionally they scavenge carrion.

Dasyurids will also defend themselves aggressively, while growling, shrieking and hissing. Even the tiniest will attack and bite humans in self-defence.

Above: A Common Planigale (*Planigale maculata*) is devouring a grasshopper. Planigales are among the smallest Australian marsupials. One species, the Long-tailed Planigale (*Planigale ingrami*), is one of the smallest mammals in the world. The body of a Long-tailed Planigale is 5–6 cm long and it weighs about the same as a 10-cent coin.

Conservation Watch

Six species of dasyurids are Endangered. Their small size makes them easy targets for feral predators such as cats. Habitat loss due to grazing and weed invasion also threatens their existence.

BUSHY-TAILED CLIMBERS

Phascogales (*Phascogale* species) are among the most distinctive of the small dasyurids because of their bushy, "bottle-brush" tails.

They are extremely agile climbers and can leap up to 2 m between trees. Phascogales can run up, down, around and under tree branches with ease because the soles of their feet are ridged to help them grip the bark and they have an inner hind toe that acts like a thumb.

Although they seldom feed on the ground, phascogales will occasionally leave their arboreal homes to attack poultry and caged birds. They hunt by night and shelter in tree hollows during the day.

Above: The Brush-tailed Phascogale (*Phascogale tapoatafa*) occurs in many areas of northern, eastern and south-west Australia. However, it is rarely seen.

the FACTS!

MANY SMALL MAMMALS store body fat to sustain them during the winter or when food is scarce. The Fat-tailed Dunnart (*Sminthopsis crassicaudata*), is able to store food in its tail (below). During good seasons, the dunnart's tail becomes enlarged and carrot-shaped.

Below: The Kowari (*Dasyuroides byrnei*) lives in the Channel Country of Queensland and the Simpson Desert of Central Australia. It hunts insects, frogs and reptiles, but will also take a much larger animal up to the size of a Long-haired Rat (*Rattus villosissimus*). The Kowari spends the daylight hours in a burrow, sometimes in one dug by other mammals, and does not need to drink.

THE FATAL BREEDING SEASON

Some small dasyurids have very short lives due to a quirk of nature, in which the males die after breeding. Antechinuses (*Antechinus* species) are the most extreme example of this, with almost every male dying at one year old.

During the two-week breeding season, the noisy, aggressive males expend enormous amounts of energy seeking females, mating and fighting off other males. Unfortunately, the stress of mating eventually proves too much and causes their immune systems to fail. They fall victim to parasites, stomach ulcers and bacterial infections and most die long before their offspring are born. Female antechinuses are luckier. They usually survive until the following year, but they do not breed as successfully.

Phascogales follow a similar breeding cycle, but quolls, planigales and dunnarts are more flexible and live to breed over a few years.

Some dasyurid females have a pouch, while others merely have a fold of skin over the teats. The newborns attach to a teat and remain there until they are too big to be dragged around. When this happens they climb onto the mother's back, gripping her fur tightly. If a young animal falls off, it will call until the mother returns to retrieve it. Larger juvenile animals are left in the nest while the mother hunts.

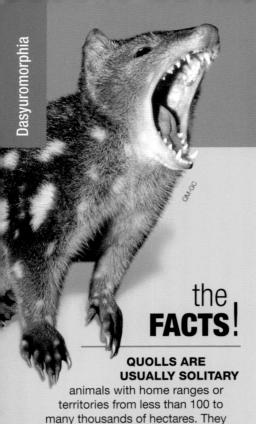

Quolls
— spotted hunters

Order: Dasyuromorphia
Meaning: *dasys* — hairy; *oura* — tail; *morphe* — form (forms of hairy-tails)

The earliest records of quolls (Dasyurus species) can be found in the journals of Captain James Cook's 1770 voyage to the east coast of Australia. The expedition's artist, Sydney Parkinson, even made a drawing of an animal known to Aborigines as a "taquol".

the
FACTS!

QUOLLS ARE USUALLY SOLITARY
animals with home ranges or territories from less than 100 to many thousands of hectares. They may travel several kilometres each night in their search for food.

MALE QUOLLS HAVE OVERLAPPING TERRITORIES
and neighbours use shared toilet sites to mark their boundaries and social status. The latrines are usually located in open spaces or on rock ledges.

QUOLLS THAT LIVE IN COOL
temperate regions are often larger than animals of the same species from warm tropical areas. The phenomenon of temperature influencing the body size of a warm-blooded animal is known as Bergman's Rule and also applies to many other creatures.

DURING THE DAY, quolls are usually content to rest in one of the many dens scattered through their territories. However, they can occasionally be seen scavenging around picnic areas and rubbish bins or basking in the sun.

THE TOXIC CANE TOAD is believed to have been partially responsible for the demise of the Northern Quoll in Queensland and the Northern Territory.

QUOLLS ARE NOT CONFINED
to Australia. Two more species of quoll occur in New Guinea — the New Guinea Quoll (*Dasyurus albopunctatus*) and the Bronze Quoll (*Dasyurus spartacus*). Little is known about these animals.

QUOLLS ARE CAT-SIZED DASYURIDS
that are easily identified by their spotted brown or black fur. Like other dasyurids, quolls have a pointed snout and a long tail.

Four species of quoll were once widely distributed across Australia. The early settlers at Port Jackson (Sydney) were familiar with quolls, even though they were confused about their true identity. They described quolls as cats, polecats, martens, opossums and rats. Since 1770, quolls have declined so dramatically in numbers and their range has been so fragmented that most Australians have not seen one in the wild. Adult quolls require large territories but there are few areas unaffected by land clearing or other human activities.

Below: Quolls usually raise six young. More may be born, but only six will be able to find a teat and the rest of the litter will die. A newborn quoll is the size of a grain of rice.

Above: The Spotted-tailed Quoll is the only species that has spots along its tail and it is also the only species with a true pouch. In other species, the young are protected by flaps of skin around the female's teats.

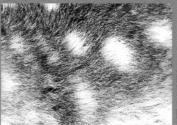

Conservation Watch

All quolls except the Northern Quoll are listed as Endangered or Vulnerable. Cane toads threaten Northern Quolls. Introduced Red Foxes now threaten the Eastern Quoll in Tasmania.

EUROPEAN SETTLEMENT OF AUSTRALIA has had a major impact on quoll numbers. Habitat loss and degradation, fire, introduced animals, disease and hunting have all contributed to quoll declines.

The Spotted-tailed or Tiger Quoll (*Dasyurus maculatus*) is the largest quoll and the largest native predator on mainland Australia. Males can reach 130 cm (total length) and can weigh 7 kg. Females are smaller, with the largest about 90 cm long and 4 kg in weight. Spotted-tailed Quolls formerly occurred in forest, heath and woodlands from Queensland's Wet Tropics to Tasmania.

The Western Quoll (*Dasyurus geoffroii*) was once the most widespread of all quolls, being found throughout arid and semi-arid regions across Australia. Unfortunately, it is now restricted to the dry forests and mallee scrub of the far south-west of Western Australia. Baiting of feral predators and fencing of habitat is allowing the Western Quoll to recover.

The Northern Quoll (*Dasyurus hallucatus*) is the smallest species. Both sexes are about 60 cm long, but males are heavier at 0.4–0.9 kg. Females weigh 0.3–0.5 kg. Northern Quolls once ranged across northern Australia from South-East Queensland to the Pilbara of Western Australia. Northern Quolls prefer rocky areas and open woodlands and are as at home in the trees as they are on the ground.

Eastern Quolls (*Dasyurus viverrinus*) were once found across much of south-eastern Australia. They are still common in Tasmania, but are almost extinct on the mainland. Eastern Quolls inhabit open forest, scrubs and heaths. They have a delicate build, fawn to black fur with white spots and a plain tail, sometimes with a white tip.

Above: A quoll's bite is stronger than that of a similar-sized dog. Quolls are vocal animals and when threatened will growl, hiss, make explosive spitting sounds and emit piercing screams that have been likened to the sound of a chainsaw.

the FACTS!

LIGHTNING SPEED and powerful jaws enable quolls to dispatch their prey with a killing bite to the head or neck, using their numerous sharp teeth.

AFTER EACH MEAL, quolls meticulously clean and groom their paws and snouts. It is not uncommon to find the skin of their prey neatly turned inside out. Although a male will challenge a female for food, he will defend the nursery den and feed his mate while she is nursing young.

QUOLLS SOMETIMES EAT FRUIT, but are primarily nocturnal hunters that prey on many different animals. Bandicoots, possums and rabbits are favoured foods for large quolls. Smaller species feed on spiders, scorpions, insects, frogs, reptiles, birds and mammals, including other dasyurids.

FEMALE DENS tend to be clustered into a smaller area and there is little overlap with the territories of other females. In contrast, male dens are widely scattered and male territories commonly overlap.

Conservation Watch

Vulnerable. Until recently, feral dogs were the major threat to devils. Now disease poses a serious risk.

Tasmanian Devil
— not so nasty

Right: A Tasmanian Devil carefully watching from behind a cover of long grass.

Order: Dasyuromorphia
Meaning: *dasys* — hairy; *oura* — tail; *morphe* — form (forms of hairy-tails)

The Tasmanian Devil (Sarcophilus harrisii) is the world's largest living marsupial carnivore. Its spine-chilling screeches, menacing jaws and reputed bad temper led the early European settlers to call it "The Devil".

the FACTS!

TASMANIAN DEVILS ARE THREATENED by an infectious cancer, the fatal devil facial tumour disease (DFTD). This disease has wiped out more than 40 per cent of wild devils, and some local populations have been reduced by as much as 90 per cent. The cancer is transmitted through bites. Disease-free devils have been sent to mainland zoos and wildlife parks as a "Noah's Ark" population.

TASMANIAN DEVILS MATE in March and 3–4 young are born in April. The female has four teats in her pouch, which opens backwards.

CONTRARY TO POPULAR OPINION, the famous "yawn" or "gape" of the Tasmanian Devil is not a threatening stance. It is performed when an individual is uncertain or feels itself under threat.

THE LIFESPAN of a Devil is about eight years.

AN ABORIGINAL MAN buried around 7000 years ago at Lake Nitchie in western NSW wore a necklace of 178 teeth that had been taken from at least 47 devils.

ALTHOUGH IT IS NOW found only in Tasmania, the Devil occurred widely on the Australian mainland until about 600 years ago.

It is a squat, thick-set animal about the size of a dog. Its fur is black, but it may have patches of white on the rump and chest. Males are larger and heavier than females (9 kg vs 7 kg) and have broader heads and thicker necks.

Tasmanian Devils are found in any habitat that allows them to hide during the day and hunt at night. They roam widely when foraging and establish well-worn trails in thick vegetation.

Devils move with a loping gait that allows them to cover around 8 km in a night.

Left: Despite its fierce appearance, a devil is no match for an average-sized domestic dog. The demise of the Devil on mainland Australia is thought to be linked to the Dingo.

NOISY WANDERERS

The Tasmanian Devil is more of a scavenger than a true hunter. It will devour its meal — bones, fur and all — using powerful jaw muscles and strong teeth. Devil diets include wallabies, small mammals, birds, frogs, insects and insect larvae. Night-feeding corbie grubs, a serious insect pest of pasture grasses, are a favourite food of the Devil.

Above: A Devil uses its second molar tooth for cracking bones and this tooth is usually worn down to a stump by the time an animal is three years old.

Dead livestock is an important food source for devils and several animals will often gather at large carcasses. (An account of 22 has been recorded feeding on a dead cow.) Such gatherings are always noisy, boisterous affairs. Rowdy behaviour helps individuals to establish dominance within the group. Like other scavengers, Devils have discovered that roadways provide food from roadkill.

Thylacine
— a "marsupial wolf"

Order: Dasyuromorphia
Meaning: *dasys* — hairy; *oura* — tail; *morphe* — form (forms of hairy-tails)

The now extinct Thylacine (Thylacinus cynocephalus) is one of Australia's most intriguing animals. It was commonly called a "Tasmanian Tiger" because of the dark stripes on its body and tail, but it actually looked more like a wolf.

TO ADD TO THE CONFUSION, although it had a wolf-like head, teeth and forelegs, its hindlegs and broad-based tail are typical marsupial characteristics. Body hair was short and soft. Females had back-opening pouches, and the young were dependent until at least half-grown.

Like the Tasmanian Devil, the Thylacine was once widespread across the Australian continent and it also occurred in New Guinea. Habitat change, the introduction of the Dingo and hunting by Aboriginal people probably also contributed to the decline of the Thylacine on the mainland. The last known Thylacine died in captivity in 1936.

The formation of Bass Strait about 8000 –10,000 years ago isolated Tasmania from the rest of Australia and temporarily ensured the Thylacine's survival. When European settlers arrived in the early 19th century with their flocks of sheep, the Thylacine faced a new threat. It was intensively hunted and poisoned to prevent it preying on sheep and on animals caught in the snare lines of fur-trappers.

Left: Early naturalist John Gould produced this illustration of a pair of Thylacines in about 1850–1851.

BACK FROM THE PAST?

It has been suggested that the DNA of preserved Thylacines could be cloned to resurrect a living animal, just like the dinosaurs in the film, *Jurassic Park*. Unfortunately, such a project is unlikely to succeed. The problems are that the DNA of the preserved animals is not intact and no suitable host exists. The "closest" living relatives of the Thylacine — quolls, Devils and Numbats — are all separated by some 25 million years of evolutionary change and are very different animals. They are also too small to qualify. Finally, the project would be extraordinarily expensive and such funding would be better used saving living species and their habitats!

the FACTS!

THYLACINUS CYNOCEPHALUS means "pouched dog with wolf's head".

THYLACINES HUNTED, alone or in pairs, at night or at dusk and used scent to track kangaroos and wallabies. They were slow-moving and relied on persistence rather than speed to catch prey. Once the prey animal was exhausted, the Thylacine would rush to the kill.

WHEN HUNTING, Thylacines communicated with a terrier-like yapping. Anxious or disturbed animals made a coughing bark.

AT LEAST 12 SPECIES of Thylacine have been identified from fossils but only one survived to the time of European settlement.

DISEASE MAY HAVE played a part in the extinction of the Thylacine. It is known that Eastern Quolls and Tasmanian Devils were affected by a disease at the beginning of the 20th century and this may also have impacted on Thylacine populations.

NAA #6180, 21/8/78/15

THE LAST KNOWN THYLACINE (above) died in captivity at Beaumaris Zoo in Hobart in 1936. It was declared extinct 50 years later in 1986.

SOME PEOPLE BELIEVE and hope that Thylacines could still exist in remote parts of Tasmania. Many people claim to have seen them, but no sightings have ever been confirmed and no physical evidence has ever been found.

Numbat
— the prettiest anteater

Right: Numbat fur is short but it is an excellent trapper of solar heat.

Order: Dasyuromorphia
Meaning: *dasys* — hairy; *oura* — tail; *morphe* — form (forms of hairy-tails)

The Numbat (Myrmecobius fasciatus) is Australia's most brightly coloured marsupial. It has reddish-brown fur on its back, a black rump and a bushy, curved tail, white stripes along the rear of its body and another dark stripe, edged in white, from its ear to its mouth.

the FACTS!

IT IS ESTIMATED that a Numbat eats around 20,000 termites each day. This specialised diet makes it difficult to keep Numbats in captivity because it is not possible to supply enough termites. Instead, researchers have created large, fenced reserves covering thousands of hectares to help protect the Numbat.

LIKE OTHER MARSUPIALS, Numbat young are born blind and hairless. Male Numbats roam extensively seeking mates before and during the January breeding season. The female does not have a pouch and carries up to four young until they are about six months old when they are left in a den. Young Numbats begin foraging for themselves at about eight months and are independent within a year. They may move 15 km or more from their place of birth.

M & I MORCOMBE

NUMBATS NEST in hollow logs or in burrows and line their nests with shredded bark and grasses. They use their mouths to carry nesting material and to move small branches.

Above: A Numbat grows to 20–27.5 cm long and weighs 300–715 g. Its bushy tail is nearly as long as its body (16.6–21 cm).

ONE OF THE COMMON NAMES for the Numbat in the past was "Banded Anteater" because of its distinctive colour, pattern and diet. An echidna eats several different types of ants, while the Numbat is the only marsupial in the world to feed on termites alone. Its long tongue laps faster than the eye can see.

Numbats once ranged across the semi-arid and arid regions of southern Australia, but fewer than 2000 still survive in the wild in the jarrah and wandoo forests of south-west Western Australia. These eucalypt trees provide the sorts of hollows and fallen logs that the Numbat needs for shelter and that termites use for food and nests.

Numbats search for termites during the daylight hours in open spaces on the forest floor. They forage alone, but always stay close to cover. Once a Numbat has found a termite nest, it digs to expose the galleries and then licks up the swarming insects with its sticky, cylindrical tongue. A Numbat's tongue is about half the length of its head and body combined.

Marsupial Mole — golden "sand-swimmers"

Conservation Watch

Endangered. Threats include feral predators, soil compaction by livestock and vehicles; and habitat change caused by fire and grazing.

Order: Notoryctemorphia
Meaning: *notos* — southern; *oryktes* — digger; *morphe* — form (forms of southern diggers)

The soft red sands of the central and north-western desert country hide one of Australia's most mysterious animals. The marsupial mole is rarely seen above ground and little is known about its life below the surface.

A DESERT SPECIALIST, the rare mole spends its entire life below the desert sands, occasionally emerging after infrequent rains. Even then, it leaves little trace of its presence and is able to quickly burrow back down into the earth. Like many other animals that live underground, the mole has adapted to life in a sunless world. It is blind and has no external ears, although it does have ear openings surrounded by thick fur. Two of the toes on each foreleg have large shovel-like claws for digging. This mole is also known as the "blind sand burrower".

BRUCE THOMSON/ANT PHOTO

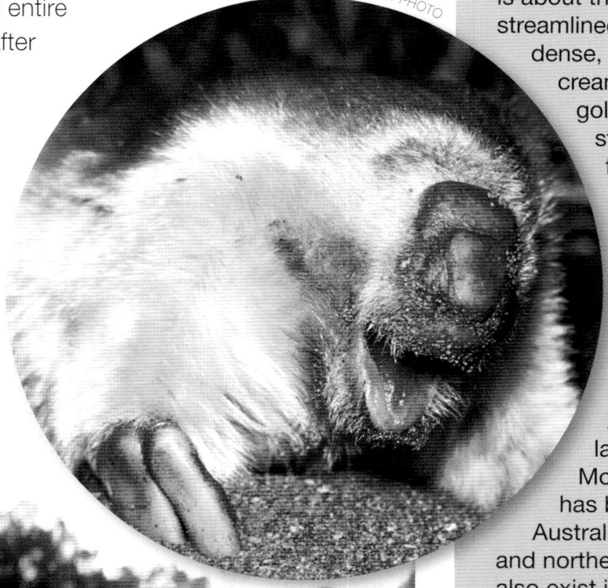

Below: When it comes to the surface, a marsupial mole leaves a characteristic track across the sand. The three wavy lines are caused by the animal's legs and tail.

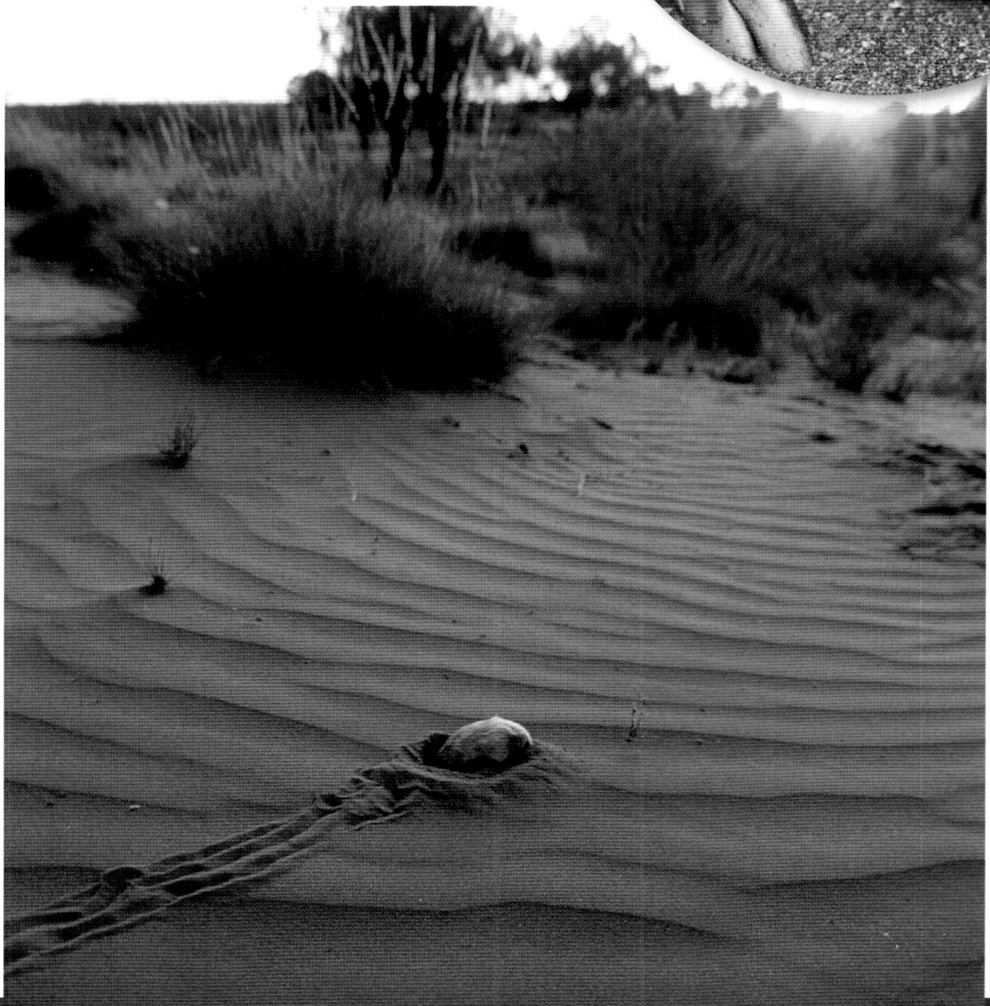

BRUCE THOMSON/ANT PHOTO

the FACTS!

THE MARSUPIAL MOLE (left), is about the size of a rat. Its streamlined body is covered in dense, shiny fur that ranges from creamy pink to yellow and pale gold. Its tail is a short, bald stub. The pouch for young faces the rear.

TWO SPECIES ARE KNOWN. The Northern Marsupial Mole (*Notoryctes caurinus*) inhabits the north-western deserts of Western Australia. The slightly larger Southern Marsupial Mole (*Notoryctes typhlops*) has been found in Western Australia, the Northern Territory and northern South Australia. It may also exist in the far south-west of Queensland.

THE MOLE IS WELL KNOWN TO ABORIGINAL PEOPLE living in Central Australia. *Itjaritjari* is the Indigenous name for the Southern Marsupial Mole and the northern species is known as *Kakarratul*.

A TOUGH SHIELD of horny skin protects the mole's snout and nose as it burrows through the soil. It usually travels 10–20 cm below the surface, but mole tunnels have been found as deep as 2 m.

MARSUPIAL MOLES are known to eat the eggs, larvae and pupae of various insects captured underground, but they may also catch other small animals when they are close to the surface.

SCIENTISTS ORIGINALLY THOUGHT the mole used its front legs to "swim" through the sand with the burrow collapsing as it moves forward. They now believe that the mole "tunnels", using it legs to push the dirt behind it.

Bandicoots
— determined diggers

Order: Peramelemorphia
Meaning: *pera* — pouch; *meles* — badger; *morphe* — form (forms of pouched badgers)

Australian homeowners, even in the suburbs, often wake to find their lawns dotted with small conical pits. These shallow holes are not burrows, but the work of hungry bandicoots that spend the night-time hours digging for beetle larvae and other food.

the FACTS!

BANDICOOTS HAVE an average life span of three years.

THE NAME BANDICOOT did not originate in Australia. It refers to three species of large Indian rats belonging to the genus *Bandicota*. The name transferred to Australian bandicoots because of their superficial resemblance to the Indian rodents.

AUSTRALIA HAS THREE species of short-nosed bandicoot (*Isoodon* species), four species of long-nosed bandicoots (*Perameles* species) and a spiny bandicoot (*Echymipera* species) found on Cape York Peninsula.

DURING THE DAY, bandicoots shelter in nests of grass and plant material placed in a depression in the ground, hidden well away in thick undergrowth.

A BANDICOOT is a small rabbit-sized marsupial that digs most of its food out of the leaf litter and soil. Bandicoots are omnivorous. They feed on insects, spiders and other small animals, as well as roots, seeds, fruit and fungi.

Bandicoots are superbly adapted for digging with strong forelegs and clawed toes, and a long pointed snout to sniff out hidden food. Their elongated hindfeet enable them to move with a galloping or bounding hop. They can bounce or leap up to a metre into the air! Their hindlegs can also deliver a powerful defensive kick if the animal is attacked or handled.

Above: The second and third toes of a bandicoot's hindfoot are fused. They are used for grooming and for defence.

FAST BREEDERS

Bandicoots have one of the shortest gestation periods — the time between mating and the birth of young — of any mammal on Earth. Gestation lasts just 12.5 days and is even faster than mice (18 days) and rabbits (28 days).

Each female can produce two or three litters of up to four young every year. Females have eight teats and a backwards-facing pouch. When the young are born they find their way to the pouch, where they attach themselves to the teats. The young remain in the pouch for about eight weeks. At this stage, young bandicoots are about the size of a rat and this makes them an easy target for cats, owls, snakes and other predators.

Bandicoots are aggressive territorial animals, particularly during the breeding season when males are noisy and get into scuffles. Breeding seasons extend from winter to summer, but may be year-round in northern Australia.

Right: When they are born, bandicoots are not much bigger than one half of a split pea.

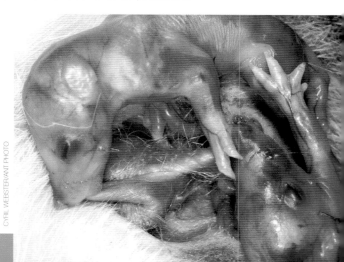

Bilbies
— burrowing bandicoots

IAN MORRIS

Order: Peramelemorphia
Meaning: *pera* — pouch; *meles* — badger; *morphe* — form (forms of pouched badgers)

Sometimes called the Australian Easter Bunny because of its large ears and soft, silky, blue-grey fur, the Greater Bilby (Macrotis lagotis) is the largest of all bandicoots. Bilbies are remarkable burrowers and build extensive tunnels under the dry sandy soils of arid Australia.

A SINGLE BILBY may construct as many as twelve burrows within its home range and will mark the entrance to each burrow with a distinctive fan-shaped mound of soil. Burrows can be up to 2 m deep.

Bilbies use their burrows to shelter from high daytime temperatures and to protect themselves from predators. They emerge only at night to forage for insects, lizards, mice, worms, snails, fruit, seeds, bulbs and some plants. Bilbies seldom drink because they obtain most of the water they need from their food.

Female bilbies tend to stay close to their burrows, but males wander further away in their search for food.

the FACTS!

THE BILBY is an important part of traditional Aboriginal culture in the deserts of Central Australia.

THE LESSER BILBY (*Macrotis leucura*) was recorded on just a handful of occasions between its discovery in 1887 and its presumed extinction during the 1950s. The last sighting of the Lesser Bilby was made in 1931. It was said to prey on small mammals such as rodents and dasyurids.

GREATER BILBIES measure 29–55 cm long and weigh 0.8–2.4 kg. The Lesser Bilby was much smaller, with a body measurement of 20–27 cm and weighed only 300–435 g.

WITCHETTY GRUBS, honeypot ants, termites and wild onion bulbs are favourite bilby foods.

BILBIES CAN BREED all year whenever conditions are suitable. Females have a backward-opening pouch with eight teats, even though they usually give birth to only one or two young at a time. The young remain in the pouch for 75 to 80 days, and are independent of the mother about two weeks after that.

PIG-FOOTED BANDICOOTS are not thought to have been common, although the species was widespread. They appear to have been principally vegetarian, taking grass seeds in the wild. By day they sheltered in a grass nest, from which they emerged in the evening to feed. Twins may have been normal, with breeding occurring between May and June.

Above: The Greater Bilby survives in scattered populations from the Pilbara and Kimberley regions of Western Australia to south-west Queensland.

A STRANGE MARSUPIAL

The extinct Pig-footed Bandicoot (*Chaeropus ecaudatus*) was one of the strangest marsupials to ever exist.

It was about the size of a kitten, had long, slender limbs and each of its hindfeet had a single, elongated toe like a tiny horse's hoof. The forefeet each had two toes and resembled the cloven hoofs of a pig, hence the common name.

Right: The last known Pig-footed Bandicoot was found in 1901, but information from Aboriginal people in remote regions suggests it may have survived until the 1950s.

Koala
— a life in the gum trees

Order: Diprotodontia
Meaning: *di* — two; *proto* — front; *dont* — tooth (two front teeth)

Above: Koalas have a thick woolly fur that protects them from temperature extremes and rain. The fur is particularly thick on the Koala's bottom and acts like a cushion.

the FACTS!

GUM TREES PRODUCE poisonous chemicals as a protection against leaf-eating animals. The Koala's digestive system is specially adapted to detoxify these poisons. Their acute sense of smell helps them identify different leaves and detect how poisonous they are.

WHEN APPROACHING a tree to climb, Koalas spring from the ground and catch their front claws in the bark, then bound upwards. Claw marks are usually visible on the trunks of trees regularly used as "home trees" by Koalas.

KOALAS ARE COMPLETELY at home in the tree tops, even when they are fast asleep on a hard branch. They have a wide variety of sitting and sleeping postures and often move around to catch the sun or the breeze. On hot days, it is common to see Koalas with limbs dangling loosely as they try to keep cool. In cold weather they curl themselves into balls to conserve their body heat.

KOALAS WALK AWKWARDLY, but they can run and even swim.

The Koala (Phascolarctos cinereus) is one of Australia's most iconic animals. Like the kangaroo, it is immediately recognised around the world as a symbol of Australia.

ITS NAME COMES from an Aboriginal word meaning "no drink" because a Koala receives more than 90 per cent of its water from the leaves that it eats. It is one of the few native mammals that can survive on a diet of eucalyptus (gum) leaves, which are toxic to most other animals.

In Australia there are more than 600 types of eucalypt trees, but Koalas eat only a small number of these. Eucalyptus leaves are very fibrous and low in nutrition. To cope with this diet, Koalas have a slow metabolic rate that allows them to retain food in their digestive systems for long periods. In this way, they can extract maximum amounts of nutrients from their food. Koalas also sleep for approximately 18 hours per day and this conserves their energy.

Above: Each Koala eats about 200–500 g of leaves per day.

BALANCING ACT

The Koala has an excellent sense of balance and its muscular body and long limbs make it an agile climber. Its climbing strength comes from the thigh muscle, which joins the shin bone at a much lower point than in other animals. Rough pads on each paw and long sharp claws help the Koala grip tree trunks and branches. Two opposable fingers on each front paw are used in much the same way as a human thumb. On each hind paw, the second and third toes are fused together to form a grooming aid.

KOALAS LIVE IN OPEN FOREST and woodland from the Atherton Tableland in far north Queensland to islands off the coast of Victoria and South Australia. They can also be found in dry woodlands west of the Great Dividing Range, but do not occur in arid or desert lands.

Koalas are highly territorial and live in stable breeding groups. However, they are also solitary animals within a network of overlapping territories. Each Koala maintains a home range around a number of favoured "food trees". These trees also provide shelter and places for contact with other Koalas. Since European settlement, approximately 80 per cent of Australia's eucalypt forests have been cleared, fragmented or degraded, particularly along the east coast.

Above: Koalas are most active from dusk to dawn when they are less likely to lose precious moisture and energy because of the cooler temperatures at this time of day.

SOMETHING TO SAY

Koalas use sound to communicate with one another. Males make a deep grunting bellow to signify their social status. Females make a more low-pitched bellow. Mothers and babies make soft clicking, squeaking and murmuring sounds to each other. All Koalas will cry or scream in fear. Koalas also communicate by marking their trees with their scent.

Left: Young Koalas are known as "joeys".

Right: Fur colour varies from light grey to brown with patches of white on the chest and neck, inside the arms and legs, and inside the ears. Mature males have a brown "scent gland" in the centre of the chest.

YUMMY POO

Before they are old enough to eat gum leaves, young Koalas first feed on milk and then on a soft, runny substance called "pap", which the mother produces in her own body.

"Pap" is essentially a special form of faeces, or poo, which allows the mother to pass on the micro-organisms that are essential for digesting poisonous eucalypt leaves.

Koalas breed during the spring and summer from September to March. Females are ready to breed at about three or four years old. The gestation period is 34–36 days. Koalas usually produce one offspring each year, but some give birth only every two or three years.

the FACTS!

DISEASE POSES A SERIOUS THREAT to Koala colonies around the country. Scientists have discovered that a micro-organism called chlamydia causes conjunctivitis, pneumonia and other infections that reduce the Koalas' ability to breed. In some areas, disease-free Koalas have been introduced to local colonies to boost population levels. Koalas are also known to suffer from leukaemia and skin cancer.

Wombats
— nature's "earthmovers"

Order: Diprotodontia
Meaning: *di* — two; *proto* — front; *dont* — tooth (two front teeth)

Wombats are among the largest burrowing mammals in the world. They have a distinctive stocky shape, a blunt head, small eyes and ears, and a short muscular neck. Like other burrowing animals, wombats have powerful legs and sharp claws for digging.

the FACTS!

IF A WOMBAT IS THREATENED it dives head first into its burrow or a hollow log so that its rump, which is covered with tough skin, is facing its attacker. If a predator follows a wombat into its burrow, the predator risks being crushed between the wombat and the burrow roof or wall.

THE FRONT TEETH of a wombat are rootless. This means they are constantly growing and are never worn away. Wombats are able to chew grasses well into their old age.

WOMBATS ARE OFTEN CONSIDERED to be slow-moving, dozy animals, but when necessary a wombat can run at 40 km/h over short distances.

COMMON WOMBATS that live in the Australian Alps have to dig through snow to find food in winter.

THE WOMBAT'S CLOSEST relative is the Koala.

Above: Wombats grow to about 1.3 m long and can weigh up to 36 kg. They are also relatively long-lived and have been known to live for up to 27 years in captivity.

WOMBATS HAVE EXISTED in Australia for millions of years, but there are only three living species: the Common Wombat (*Vombatus ursinus*), the Southern Hairy-nosed Wombat (*Lasiorhinus latifrons*) and the Northern Hairy-nosed Wombat (*Lasiorhinus krefftii*).

As their name suggests, Hairy-nosed wombats have hairy noses. Their ears are longer and more pointy than those of a Common Wombat and they have long, square snouts.

The Common Wombat lives mainly in wet forests along the coast and ranges of eastern Australia, from southern Queensland to Tasmania.

Right: In the past, farmers and graziers considered wombat burrows a danger to livestock and because of this thousands of wombats were killed. Land clearing still reduces their range.

Hairy-nosed wombats are rare. The southern species prefer dry open country in South Australia, New South Wales and Western Australia. The Northern Hairy-nosed Wombat was thought to be extinct until a small population was discovered near Clermont in Queensland.

Wombats are grazers. They spend between three and eight hours each night feeding on the native grasses that are their favourite food, such as wallaby grass and kangaroo grass.

MICHAEL CERMAK

Conservation Watch

The Northern Hairy-nosed Wombat is Endangered and the Southern Hairy-nosed Wombat may be Vulnerable. Threats include loss of habitat, vehicle strikes, feral predators and grazing.

SETTING OUT TERRITORY

Wombats construct burrows in well-drained soils that are easy to dig. The burrows, which are often built on the sides of gullies, can be up to 30 m long and several metres deep. Wombats generally stay in their burrows during the day to keep warm in winter and cool in summer. The home range of wombats varies from 4 to 23 ha around their burrows.

Although they will share burrows, wombats are possessive about their feeding grounds and mark their boundaries with scent trails and droppings. If a wombat intrudes on another's territory, it will be discouraged with a series of snorts, screeches and even a chase. The wombat population of an area is dependent on the number of available feeding grounds. A young wombat can sometimes take the place of an adult that has died, but usually it will have to find its own feeding ground.

Right: A wombat has an energy efficient life cycle. When resting they can slow their metabolism to two-thirds of its normal rate. This helps regulate their body temperature and also helps to conserve water.

GROWING UP

Wombats usually breed from September to December, although this varies slightly according to the species. Newborn wombats are tiny, being less than 3 cm long and weighing only about 1 g. They stay in the pouch for between 7 and 10 months and are not fully independent until they are about 15 months old.

A wombat's pouch faces backwards. This stops dirt and twigs getting caught in it when the mother is digging.

Little is known about wombat breeding habits and they are difficult to breed in captivity. This is one of the problems facing researchers trying to protect the endangered Northern Hairy-nosed Wombat, which gives birth to one joey during the northern wet season (November–April).

the FACTS!

A WOMBAT USES its forepaws for digging and, after pushing the dirt to one side, it will back out of its burrow moving the loose dirt with both the front and back paws as it goes.

THE FUR OF COMMON WOMBATS varies in colour from light grey to black and is sometimes flecked with tan.

ONLY ABOUT 118 Northern Hairy-nosed Wombats remain in the wild and they are now restricted to a protected reserve at Epping Forest in central Queensland. However, fossils show that the wombat once lived over much of eastern Australia.

A WOMBAT CAN DIG about 2 m of burrow every night. A burrow may be 30 m long, about 50 cm high and 50 cm wide, and it may have several entrances.

THERE ARE THREE subspecies of the Common Wombat: *Vombatus ursinus hirsutus*, which is found on the mainland; *Vombatus ursinus tasmaniensis*, which is found in Tasmania; and *Vombatus ursinus ursinus*, which was once found throughout the Bass Strait islands, but is now restricted to Flinders Island.

IAN MORRIS

Ringtail possums
— hanging around

Order: Diprotodontia
Meaning: *di* — two; *proto* — front; *dont* — tooth (two front teeth)

The Common Ringtail Possum (Pseudocheirus peregrinus), like its close relative the Brushtail Possum, is one of the few Australian native animals able to live in close contact with humans.

IT IS A FAMILIAR night-time animal in city parks and backyards, where it scurries along powerlines in search of food trees and can often be seen perched high on the roofs of suburban homes. Ringtails communicate with a twittering chirrup, a chattering alarm call, and a grunt when fighting. They live about five years in the wild. Unlike many native animals, the Common Ringtail Possum is able to take advantage of the opportunities created by living near humans.

the FACTS!

ROCK RINGTAIL POSSUMS (*Petropseudes dahli*) live among rocky escarpments across northern Australia and are equally at home climbing over boulders and up rock faces as they are in trees (above). During the day, these sociable possums shelter in rock crevices and under deep ledges, emerging at night to feed on leaves and fruit.

DURING DAYLIGHT HOURS, the Common Ringtail Possum sleeps in a spherical nest called a "drey", which is made from grass and shredded bark. The drey is usually located in a tree hole, tree fork or dense foliage. Several individuals may share the one nest.

THE TAIL of a Common Ringtail Possum is about two-thirds the length of the body.

GREATER GLIDERS (*Petauroides volans*) below, are related to ringtail possums, not other gliders. They have large, furred ears.

QM-GC

Above: A Common Ringtail Possum is about the size of a cat, with grey-brown body fur and a white belly. It has white patches behind its ears and a white tip on its tail.

A TAIL FOR CLIMBING

The Common Ringtail has a long prehensile tail that it uses like a fifth limb to curl around branches, poles and posts as it climbs and jumps between trees, buildings and powerlines. It also has a gap between its second and third fingers that allows it to grasp branches and other objects securely.

Although the Common Ringtail Possum eats a wide range of native and introduced plant leaves, flowers and fruits, it will also eat its own droppings. This allows the possum to digest its food twice, extracting the maximum amount of nutrients possible. Common Ringtail Possums are notorious for eating the buds of roses in gardens.

QM

ROCK RINGTAIL POSSUM MOTHERS often use their bodies as a bridge for their young to cross gaps between branches. No other possum does this.

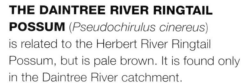

Conservation Watch

Most species of ringtail possum are Secure, but the Western Ringtail Possum (*Pseudocheirus occidentalis*) left, of south-west Western Australia is Vulnerable.

Above: Daintree River Ringtail.

Above: Lemuroid Ringtail.

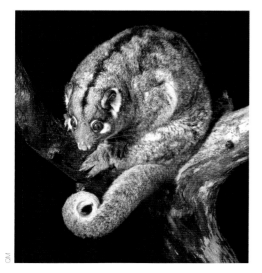

Above: Green Ringtail.

AT HOME IN THE TROPICS

The Wet Tropics region of north-east Queensland has more ringtail possums than anywhere else in Australia. Four unusual species that live in isolated groups in the high mountain rainforests are unique to the area. All are rare and all are vulnerable to habitat disturbance such as logging (tree-felling) or cyclone damage.

HERBERT RIVER RINGTAILS

(*Pseudochirulus herbertensis*) undergo a colour change as they grow. The young are pale brown, changing to stark black and white or all black when they mature. By day they sleep in nests in fern clumps or tree hollows high in the forest canopy. Two young are born and they stay in the mother's pouch for almost four months. The mother carries them around on her back for another two weeks and then they are ready to strike out on their own.

THE DAINTREE RIVER RINGTAIL

POSSUM (*Pseudochirulus cinereus*) is related to the Herbert River Ringtail Possum, but is pale brown. It is found only in the Daintree River catchment.

THE LEMUROID RINGTAIL

(*Hemibelideus lemuroides*) is a large possum that does spectacular free-fall leaps between the forest branches, using its long tail as a rudder to steer the way. It occurs only above 550 m elevation on the Atherton and Carbine Tablelands.

As its name suggests, the **GREEN RINGTAIL POSSUM** (*Pseudochirops archeri*) looks green, but this is an optical illusion caused by the arrangement of black, white and yellow bands of fur. Unlike other ringtails, a Green Ringtail Possum does not build a nest. Instead, it simply curls itself into a large ball and relies on its colour to hide it among the foliage. Green Ringtails give birth to a single young, which stays with the mother for about 10 months. Green Ringtails are threatened by potential heatwaves and reduced rainfall caused by global warming, as are all other rainforest possums.

the FACTS!

IN THE WET TROPICS ringtail possums all coexist by either frequenting different areas or feeding on different types of plants.

THE GREEN RINGTAIL POSSUM has huge salivary glands that allow it to detoxify the plant matter on which it feeds. Rock Ringtails probably lick termite mounds for much the same reason.

THE EMBLEM of the Queensland Parks and Wildlife Service is the Herbert River Ringtail (below) which is affectionately known as "Herbie".

COMMON RINGTAIL Possums are good parents. Both the male and the female care for their offspring and the male will carry the young on his back while the female is feeding.

POSSUMS AND OTHER arboreal mammals are frequently killed when crossing roads. In some areas of Queensland's Wet Tropics, rope ladders or "overpasses" have been strung high above the roadways to connect the tree canopies. This enables the possums to pass safely over the ladders and so road kills have been reduced.

Conservation Watch

All Common Brushtail Possums are Secure, but they are known to be declining in the north and west of their range.

JIRI LOCHMAN

the FACTS!

THE SCALY-TAILED POSSUM (*Wyulda squamicaudata*) above, is a rare species found only among rocky outcrops in the Kimberley region of Western Australia.

IN NEW ZEALAND, Common Brushtails are a serious feral pest in native forests, causing extensive defoliation. The possums were introduced from Australia in the 1800s with the intention of establishing a fur trade. It is estimated that around 70 million possums now live in New Zealand.

THERE ARE TWO other species of brushtail possum. The Short-eared Brushtail Possum (*Trichosurus caninus*) and the Mountain Brushtail Possum (right) are larger, darker and have smaller, more rounded ears than the Common Brushtail Possum.

Order: Diprotodontia
Meaning: *di* — two; *proto* — front; *dont* — tooth (two front teeth)

The Common Brushtail Possum (Trichosurus vulpecula) *is the most widely distributed large Australian possum species. Like ringtail possums, it has made itself at home in our cities, towns and suburbs.*

IN THE WILD, brushtail possums inhabit hollow tree limbs in woodlands and open forests, and eat leaves, grasses, herbs, flowers, fruits and insects. Around human dwellings, brushtails shelter in any suitable nook or cranny and will also shelter in roof spaces, where they can be noisy neighbours.

City parks, picnic spots and camping grounds are favourite hunting grounds, and brushtails are known to raid rubbish bins, visit bird feeders and even help themselves to pet food. In urban areas, Common Brushtail Possums have been photographed feeding with introduced Black Rats (*Rattus rattus*) and they will also raid birds' nests for the eggs.

GREG HARM

BREEDING

Brushtails are not social animals and for most of the year they lead solitary lives, only coming together at breeding time. Mating occurs during the autumn months, but births have been recorded for every month of the year. Only one young is usually born, although twins have been recorded. The young possum stays inside the mother's pouch until it is about four months old and well furred. After this time, it may be seen travelling around on its mother's back.

Brushtail possums have eleven scent glands that provide information to other possums about their identity, sex and breeding condition.

Left: Female Mountain Brushtail Possum (*Trichosurus cunninghami*) with young.

Cuscuses
— a possum in disguise

Order: Diprotodontia
Meaning: *di* — two; *proto* — front; *dont* — tooth (two front teeth)

Although the cuscus may look like the slow-moving sloths of South America and has a similar lifestyle high in the tree tops, it is really a possum. Like other possums, it can cling upside down to branches.

ABOUT 15 SPECIES of cuscuses live in New Guinea, Sulawesi and the surrounding islands, but only two occur in Australia and these are found in the rainforests of Cape York Peninsula.

Cuscuses are shy, solitary animals that emerge at night to feed on leaves, fruit, flowers, insects and other small animals in the forest canopy. By day, they hide in ferns and tree hollows, or sleep under temporary shelters of leaves or perched on a tree branch. They are seldom seen because they rarely venture to the ground.

A cuscus has a flat face, short ears and dense woolly fur on its body and limbs. Like other possums, the cuscus uses its long prehensile tail as a climbing aid. Most cuscuses are large animals, with a head and body length of around 60 cm. Cuscuses communicate with each other by guttural screeches and grunts.

Left: Cuscuses mainly live in trees, but this does not mean that they do not travel on the ground. A radio-tracked Common Spotted Cuscus travelled for about 150 m across a dirt road and over burnt grassland.

PAVEL GERMAN/ANT PHOTO

the FACTS!

THE SOUTHERN COMMON CUSCUS (below), only occurs in the Iron and McIlwraith Ranges of mid-eastern Cape York Peninsula. The Common Spotted Cuscus occurs on northern Cape York between Iron Range and Bamaga.

LITTLE IS KNOWN about the life cycle of the cuscus. They are thought to breed throughout the year, rather than during a single season. Two to four babies may be born, but only one eventually survives in the pouch.

THE SPOTTED CUSCUS will eat meat and eggs in captivity. This suggests that it eats eggs, nestling birds and perhaps other small animals in the wild.

THE LONG PREHENSILE tail of the cuscus has rough, rasp-like scales on the inside surface and no fur at all on the lower half. This adaptation helps the animal grip branches as it moves through the trees.

CUSCUSES WERE FIRST DESCRIBED in the 16th century by Portuguese explorer Antonio Galvao on the island of Molucca to Australia's north.

A SPLASH OF COLOUR

The Common Spotted Cuscus (*Spilocuscus maculatus*) is covered in white or light-coloured fur and has bright splotches of chestnut and black on its back. Its legs are reddish-brown.

The Southern Common Cuscus (*Phalanger intercastellanus*) is grey-brown above and white below with a black stripe from between the eyes to the middle of the back. With its lighter build and larger ears, the Southern Common Cuscus looks more like a variegated possum.

All cuscuses have five toes on each foot and four of the toes have claws. The two innermost toes are thumblike to make climbing along branches an easy task.

Pygmy-possums
— life at the top

Order: Diprotodontia
Meaning: *di* — two; *proto* — front; *dont* — tooth (two front teeth)

Pygmy-possums are well named — being the smallest of all possums — most species are not much larger than mice. The tiniest, the Little Pygmy-possum (Cercartetus lepidus), *weighs a mere 6–10 g and measures 6–7 cm long.*

PYGMY-POSSUMS SPEND most of their lives in the canopies of trees and in shrubs. They are nimble climbers and all have prehensile tails and padded feet with flexible toes. Most also have a thumb-like first toe on each hindfoot to help them grasp branches. Despite these adaptations for climbing, pygmy-possums can sometimes also be found on the ground, where they dart around like mice.

Pygmy-possums are nocturnal, searching for food at night and sleeping in tree hollows and other nests during the day. Little Pygmy-possums have even been found nesting under spinifex hummocks (spiny tussock grasses) in the mallee country of southern Australia. Old bird nests are another favourite retreat.

the FACTS!

MOST PYGMY-POSSUMS give birth to four young in the spring, although litter sizes may range from one to six and are dependent on seasonal conditions and the amount of food available. The young are independent by late summer.

THE LONG-TAILED Pygmy-possum (below) is the only species that occurs in the rainforest. It shares the tree canopy with a similar-looking rodent, the Tree Mouse (*Pogonomys* sp.). The two animals also have similar habitats and are difficult to tell apart, but the possum has more black around the eyes and larger ears.

PYGMY-POSSUMS are usually mousey-grey, with the exception of the Western Pygmy-possum, which is cinnamon coloured.

PYGMY-POSSUM FOSSILS dating to about 25 million years ago have been found at the Riversleigh fossil deposits in north-west Queensland. The fossils show that pygmy-possums have not changed very much in millions of years.

Above: Eastern Pygmy-possums range from southern Queensland to South Australia and feed mainly on nectar and pollen from eucalypts, banksias and bottlebrush trees. They also eat insects, seeds and fruit.

SLOW AND SLEEPY

Their small body size means that pygmy-possums must find ways to conserve body heat and energy, especially those living in cooler climates.

Eastern and Little Pygmy-possums go into torpor during cold spells in southern Australia. Torpor is the means by which an animal is able to reduce its energy loss by lowering its metabolism and body temperature to near that of its surroundings. Unlike true hibernation, torpidity generally only lasts for a few days at a time.

The Mountain Pygmy-possum is the only Australian marsupial that truly hibernates.

Conservation Watch

The Mountain Pygmy-possum is Endangered. Threats: loss of habitat, feral predators, drought and global warming. All other species are considered to be Secure.

THERE ARE FIVE SPECIES of pygmy-possum. Four inhabit forests and woodlands in different parts of the continent and one lives high in the Australian Alps.

The Long-tailed Pygmy-possum (*Cercartetus caudatus*) is restricted to the Wet Tropics of north Queensland. Three species — the Little Pygmy-possum (*Cercartetus lepidus*), Eastern Pygmy-possum (*Cercartetus nanus*) and Western Pygmy-possum (*Cercartetus concinnus*) — range across southern and south-eastern Australia.

The rare Mountain Pygmy-possum (*Burramys parvus*) is thought to occur in an area of only 10 sq km in high country covering the New South Wales–Victorian border! This limited range mainly coincides with the ski resort area.

the FACTS!

THE LITTLE PYGMY-POSSUM (below) was once thought to be restricted to Tasmania, but has now also been found on the Australian mainland in many different habitats, including the mallee country of South Australia and Victoria. It builds its nest from bark and leaves.

LIFE IN THE SNOW

The Mountain Pygmy-possum lives on the ground in boulder fields on the highest mountains of the Australian Alps. Less than 500 adult animals are believed to exist and two populations are found within ski resort areas. The possums occasionally enter huts and chalets, where there is always a risk they might be mistaken for feral rats or mice.

A Mountain Pygmy-possum's life revolves around surviving cold, snowy winters. It must make the most of the short alpine spring and summer months to build up fat reserves. At the same time it stores caches of seeds and nuts for the winter. The weight of an adult may vary from 30 g in spring up to 80 g in autumn as it fattens up for winter hibernation.

Right: The Mountain Pygmy-possum was thought to be extinct until rediscovered in 1966 in a ski chalet at Mt Higginbotham in Victoria.

DESPITE THEIR SMALL SIZE, Mountain Pygmy-possums may move up to 3 km in their search for patches of suitable habitat. They favour heathland where the native Mountain Plum Pine (*Podocarpus lawrencei*) grows, but the introduction of exotic blackberry bushes to the high country has altered much of their natural environment.

DURING HIBERNATION, the Mountain Pygmy-possum can reduce its metabolic rate by about 98 per cent. At the beginning of winter, hibernation might last only for a few days, but later in the season it may be as long as three weeks.

THE MIGRATORY BOGONG MOTH (*Agrotis infusa*) is an important source of food for the Mountain Pygmy-possum.

THE FOOD CACHES of the Mountain Pygmy-possum are a rare trait for a marsupial animal.

TINY OMNIVORES

Insects form a large part of the diet of all pygmy-possums. They are also known to eat other invertebrate animals, such as spiders and millipedes, along with nectar, fruit and seeds from native plants.

Left: Pygmy-possums lick nectar from native flowers, such as banksias. The possums feed in short bursts and then spend time grooming themselves.

Striped Possums
— flamboyant acrobats

Order: Diprotodontia
Meaning: *di* — two; *proto* — front; *dont* — tooth (two front teeth)

The Striped Possum (Dactylopsila trivirgata) is a creature of the rainforest. It is not only one of Australia's most attractive animals, it is also one of the most agile, performing spectacular leaps from high forest branches.

the FACTS!

THE CALLS OF STRIPED POSSUMS can be described as loud, harsh, guttural shrieks.

LIKE MANY OTHER POSSUMS and gliders, Striped Possums make leafy nests in tree hollows. Occasionally, both members of a pair will share the same hollow.

THE BLACK AND WHITE COLOURING of the Striped Possum resembles that of New World skunks and African zorillas. The possum can also produce a pungent musky odour. This smell may act as a deterrent to predators, causing the possums to be distasteful.

THE HOME RANGE of a male Striped Possum is much smaller (5–6.5 ha) than that of a female (21 ha).

THE END OF THE LEAP is advertised with an unmistakable crashing sound as the possum lands in palms, vines and saplings in the rainforest understorey.

As nocturnal animals, the possums are seldom seen, despite their distinctive black and white striped fur, which blends into the shadows of the forest. The noise of Striped Possums tearing into wood is often the first indication of their presence.

During the day Striped Possums shelter in leafy nests built inside tree hollows or in clumps of epiphyte plants. Mating occurs between February and August and up to two young are born. Little is known about the social behaviour of this spectacular little possum.

Right: The coat pattern of individual Striped Possums varies and is more pronounced in younger rather than older adults.

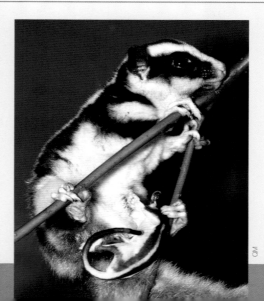

INSECTS AND THEIR LARVAE are the Striped Possum's favourite food. The possum uses a heel-like bone on each wrist to tap wood and locate insect larvae. Its acute hearing can detect if a larva responds to the tapping. The possum then tears into the surrounding timber with its strong incisor teeth and uses its elongated fourth "finger" to extract the larva from the wood.

Left: Striped Possum mother with young. An adult will eat flowers, fruits, pollen and native bee honey.

— a small mystery

Conservation Watch

Secure. Local threats include fire, loss of habitat, land clearing, harvesting of wildflowers, vehicle strikes and cats.

Order: Diprotodontia
Meaning: *di* — two; *proto* — front; *dont* — tooth (two front teeth)

A landscape rich in native wildflowers is the ideal environment for the Honey Possum (Tarsipes rostratus), *a tiny arboreal mammal that is not really a possum at all.*

Above: The snout of a Honey Possum is very long and pointed, perfect for slipping deep into flowers. This possum has three brown stripes along its back.

THE HONEY POSSUM may not be closely related to any other group of marsupials. It is the only member of the family Tarsipedidae and is therefore something of a mystery.

The Honey Possum is often found in heathland where there is a profusion of banksias, dryandras, grevilleas and hakeas. It feeds exclusively on nectar and pollen, which are collected on its brush-tipped tongue. The plants benefit from Honey Possum visits too, because the animals act as pollinators, much like nectar-feeding birds and insects. Honey Possums are very quick and agile and will dart from flower to flower when feeding.

Left: Honey Possums are mainly active at night, but can sometimes be seen during the day if conditions are right. They shelter in tree hollows, old bird nests, or other suitable crevices.

the FACTS!

THE HONEY POSSUM is not much bigger than a mouse. It measures 45–110 mm from head to tail and weighs between 12 g (males) and 22 g (females).

LIKE ALL SMALL warm-blooded animals, the Honey Possum loses body heat very quickly. This means it needs to feed constantly on high-energy foods when active. Honey Possums cannot survive in areas where nectar and pollen are lacking for even a short time and, in cold weather, they become torpid.

NOOLBENGER is the Aboriginal name for the Honey Possum.

HONEY POSSUMS BREED throughout the year and raise two to four young, but if pollen cannot be sourced, reproduction declines.

EXPANDED TIPS on their toes and fingers help Honey Possums climb. Joined toes on their hindfeet are used for grooming.

POLLEN LICKED OFF FLOWERS is scraped off the tongue with the canine teeth and ridges on the top of the mouth. It takes about six hours for a Honey Possum to digest pollen. Captive Honey Possums will feed on mealworms, but there is no evidence of them taking insects in the wild.

EVEN THE OLDEST FOSSILS of Honey Possums from the Late Pleistocene Period, about 33,000 years ago, are no help in tracing the origin of the animal or how it is related to other marsupials.

M & I MORCOMBE

Gliders
— "flying" possums

Order: Diprotodontia
Meaning: *di* — two; *proto* — front; *dont* — tooth (two front teeth)

Bats are the only mammals that can truly fly, but many tree-dwelling animals, including the gliding possums, have also developed the ability to move through the air as if they are flying.

the FACTS!

SUGAR GLIDERS, Squirrel Gliders, Mahogany Gliders and Yellow-bellied Gliders have their gliding membranes attached between their wrists and ankles.

WHEN NOT IN USE, the gliding membrane is folded against the side of the possum's body.

THE YELLOW-BELLIED GLIDER can cover distances of up to 140 m in one leap. The Sugar Glider and Squirrel Glider can reach about 50 m.

LEADBEATER'S POSSUM (*Gymnobelideus leadbeateri*) belongs to the "wrist-winged" group of gliders, but it does not glide. For many years this possum was thought to be extinct, but it was rediscovered in 1961. The diet of the Leadbeater's Possum is similar to other gliders, but it eats more plant sap and depends on tall eucalypt forests — especially old-growth trees — for food and shelter.

MOST GLIDERS have one or two young at a time, although the Feathertail Glider can have a litter of up to four young, while the Greater Glider has only one.

SOME SPECIES, particularly the Greater Glider, mark out their territory by using scent glands. They rub these glands against the trees to warn off intruders and mark territories.

Right: Sugar Gliders resting in a tree hollow.

A GLIDER uses a thin flexible sheet of skin (membrane), stretched between its forelimbs and ankles, to control the direction and speed of its movement from tree to tree.

This type of movement is called "volplaning" and differs from true flight in that the possum is not able to propel itself through the air like a bird or insect.

In Australia, there are three groups of gliding possums: the greater gliders, which are related to ringtail possums; the feathertail gliders related to pygmy-possums; and the "wrist-winged gliders". In most species of wrist-winged gliders, the skin membrane begins at the wrist.

But in other gliding possums, it starts at the elbow.

Gliders begin their "flight" by leaping downwards to gain speed. Then they level off and, using their long, well-furred tails as rudders, they steer to the next tree. Gliders land "nose up" with their feet outstretched to grasp the tree trunk as they land.

Possums are not the only animals that are able to glide. In other parts of the world, particularly in tropical rainforests, squirrels, lizards, frogs, snakes and even ants also use this type of locomotion.

Below: The Squirrel Glider is about the size of a large rat and has soft grey fur with a black stripe along the middle of its head and body.

IAN MORCOMBE

Conservation Watch

The Mahogany Glider and Leadbeater's Possum are Endangered and the Yellow-bellied Glider (northern subspecies) is Vulnerable. Threats include land clearing, habitat degradation and feral and domestic predators.

SUGAR AND SQUIRREL GLIDERS

The Sugar Glider (*Petaurus breviceps*) (above) lives in groups of up to 10 animals and nests in tree hollows. It is the most widespread of the four "wrist-winged" gliders, ranging from the Kimberley region in Western Australia to Tasmania.

Squirrel Gliders (*Petaurus norfolcensis*) are very similar to Sugar Gliders both in appearance and life cycle but they are larger and have a longer muzzle. Unlike Sugar Gliders, their tails are never white-tipped.

GREATER GLIDER

The Greater Glider (*Petauroides volans*) is the largest of the gliding possums (above), weighing between 170 g and 900 g. It lives in the open forests and woodlands of eastern Australia where eucalypts are abundant.

Greater Gliders are solitary nocturnal animals that feed on the growing tips, blossoms and buds of eucalypts.

The Greater Glider has the fluffiest ears of any glider, a long shaggy coat and a very long tail. It can be cream, grey or brown to black with a white belly. When gliding it can turn as much as 90 degrees!

FEATHERTAIL GLIDER

The Feathertail Glider (*Acrobates pygmaeus*) is the smallest gliding mammal in the world (above), with an average weight of only 12 g. It has a distinctive feather-like tail fringed with long stiff hairs and can glide more than 20 m at a time. Feathertails feed on pollen, nectar and insects. They occur in forest and woodland throughout eastern Australia.

Feathertail Gliders have large serrated toe pads to help them cling to the smooth bark of some eucalypt species.

MAHOGANY AND YELLOW-BELLIED GLIDERS

Yellow-bellied Gliders (*Petaurus australis*) are the largest of the four "wrist-winged" gliders, with a body length of about 280 mm. They inhabit only rich forest ecosystems that provide a continual supply of food.

The rare Mahogany Glider (*Petaurus gracilis*) was thought extinct for more than 100 years before it was rediscovered in 1989. It lives in low woodland on swampy coastal plains, beach ridges and melaleuca swamps in Queensland's Wet Tropics.

Left: Yellow-bellied Gliders leave distinctive "V" shaped notches on trees when collecting sap.

Right: About 2000 Mahogany Gliders are thought to survive in the wild between the towns of Tully and Ingham in far north Queensland.

Red Kangaroo
— largest living marsupial

Order: Diprotodontia
Meaning: *di* — two; *proto* — front; *dont* — tooth (two front teeth)

Red Kangaroos (Macropus rufus) *are the largest living kangaroos and largest living marsupials. Although they are smaller than some fossil species, Red Kangaroos give an indication of what Australia's megafauna (animals that lived in prehistoric times), may have looked like.*

LARGE MALES may stand nearly 1.5 m tall and weigh up to 85 kg. Females reach 1.1 m and weigh 35 kg. Males and females may differ in colour. Males are reddish and females grey, although both tend to be a reddish colour in parts of Central Australia.

Their size, long pointed ears, white cheek stripe and black and white muzzle distinguish them from other kangaroos. They hop with the body held almost horizontal to the ground and the tail curved gently upwards.

the FACTS!

KANGAROOS AND WALLABIES that belong to the family Macropodidae are commonly referred to as "macropods". They graze on grass and leaves and their ability to thrive on a poor diet explains why macropods live in so many parts of Australia.

IT IS BELIEVED that large macropods can bound more than 3–5 m in distance and jump as high as 2 m.

IN CAPTIVITY KANGAROOS can live for 28 years, but wild animals probably reach 20 years of age.

THE CONSTRUCTION of inland bores for livestock have helped Red Kangaroo numbers to increase.

LARGE RED KANGAROOS are still hunted for hides and meat.

RED KANGAROOS ARE ABLE to go without drinking as long as green grass is available.

FEMALE RED KANGAROOS give birth to a single joey and breeding is influenced by the availability of green feed. In drought times, some males and females become infertile. As soon as the rains come, the breeding season starts again.

Above: Red Kangaroos are common across arid and semi-arid Australia.

RED KANGAROOS are most active in the cooler hours of the day and at night. They spend the hottest periods resting in shallow scrapes in shady spots. To keep from overheating, Red Kangaroos lick saliva onto their arms and chests to cool down.

Grey kangaroos
— familiar visitors

Order: Diprotodontia
Meaning: *di* — two; *proto* — front; *dont* — tooth (two front teeth)

Grey kangaroos are probably the most familiar macropods and it is not uncommon to encounter them on the edges of major cities, on nearby farmland or in local bushland.

Above: Kangaroos were encountered by Captain James Cook when he visited the east coast of Australia in 1770. An entry in his journal for 4 August that year notes that the local Aboriginal people called the animals *Kangooroo* or *Kanguru*.

KANGAROOS RANGE from coastal forests and woodlands to the semi-arid and arid plains of Australia, although numbers vary considerably according to conditions.

Many people do not realise that there are actually two types of grey kangaroo. The Eastern Grey Kangaroo (*Macropus giganteus*) occurs from southern Cape York Peninsula to Victoria and eastern Tasmania, while the Western Grey Kangaroo (*Macropus fuliginosus*) is found from Queensland through South Australia and into the Shark Bay region of Western Australia. The two species are very similar, but Western Greys are slightly smaller, finer and darker.

Grey kangaroos feed on grasses and low-growing herbs. They sometimes graze during the day, but are most active in the early morning and evening. Grey kangaroos are often seen in family groups of three or four, but large mobs will gather whenever good grazing conditions exist. Breeding occurs in summer and the gestation period after mating is around 36 days. Joeys are weaned at 11 months.

Left: All kangaroos and wallabies have forward-opening pouches. A female can carry a newborn and an older joey at foot. She can produce two different kinds of milk for both young.

the FACTS!

THE EARS of an Eastern Grey Kangaroo are broader and less pointed than those of a Western Grey.

ON LAND, KANGAROOS can only move their hindfeet simultaneously, hence their hopping movement, but when swimming they can kick each leg independently.

THE FASTEST RECORDED speed for a kangaroo is 64 km/h and is held by a female Eastern Grey.

MALE EASTERN GREY Kangaroos have a distinctive musky odour.

DURING THE BREEDING SEASON, male kangaroos compete with each other and fights are common. Opponents clasp each other's arms and try to kick each other in the belly with the sharp claws of the hindfeet.

HOPPING USES slightly less energy than four-footed running, but this advantage is lost at low speed. To move slowly, kangaroos balance on their front paws and tail, and swing their hindlegs like a pendulum.

Antilopine Wallaroo
— the tropical "roo"

Order: Diprotodontia
Meaning: *di* — two; *proto* — front; *dont* — tooth (two front teeth)

The Antilopine Wallaroo (Macropus antilopinus) is so named because early naturalists believed its fur resembled the richly coloured, short-haired coat of African antelopes. It is the only large kangaroo found in tropical northern Australia, where it is most numerous on Cape York Peninsula.

the FACTS!

EARLY NATURALIST John Gould described the first specimens of Antilopine Wallaroos in 1842. The animals were taken from the Cobourg Peninsula in the Northern Territory.

ANTILOPINE WALLAROOS seem to favour terrain with low ridges and grassy depressions. Perennial native grasses that are available year round are a preferred food.

LARGE GRAZING ANIMALS like kangaroos are a vital part of every food chain. The loss of grazing animals anywhere in the world would have dramatic outcomes for the natural environment. In Australia, the most important grazing animals in subtropical and temperate woodlands are the grey kangaroos and, in the tropics, Antilopine Wallaroos fill this role.

ADULT FEMALES have been observed carrying large joeys at the end of spring, indicating that births may be concentrated towards the end of the wet season in northern Australia.

ALTHOUGH SLIGHTLY SMALLER than Red Kangaroos, the attractive Antilopine Wallaroos still look similar.

Unlike some kangaroo species, the Antilopine Wallaroo is not abundant, and recent studies suggest populations may be declining. The reasons for this are unknown but, if this is the case, it would be the first known decline of a large macropod species since European settlement more than 200 years ago.

Male and female Antilopine Wallaroos are different colours: males are brick red with white bellies, while females are reddish with a grey neck and shoulders.

Right: Males are nearly 1.2 m tall and weigh up to 49 kg. Females reach 0.8 m and weigh 20 kg.

Below: Antilopine Wallaroos form small mobs of less than 20 individuals and, in the non-breeding season, are segregated according to the sex of the animals, being either all-male or all-female. It is not known why the kangaroos behave like this, but diet could be a factor. Both males and females feed on large amounts of grass, but females eat significantly more low-growing herbs and flowering plants, which have a higher nutrient content.

Common Wallaroo
— a coat of many colours

Order: Diprotodontia
Meaning: *di* — two; *proto* — front; *dont* — tooth (two front teeth)

The Common Wallaroo (Macropus robustus) is a powerfully built kangaroo that often looks bigger than it really is because of its solid build and shaggy coat.

WALLAROOS OCCUR across much of Australia and are most likely to be seen in hilly, mountainous or escarpment country. They hide and rest among the rocks during the day and come out to eat grass and small shrubs at night.

the FACTS!

THE COLOUR OF COMMON WALLAROOS can be black, grey, tan, fawn, gold or reddish, depending on their location.

THE NAME "EURO" comes from an Aboriginal word, *uroo*.

DRAWINGS BY SIR JOSEPH BANKS show that the Common Wallaroo was one of three species of macropod encountered by Captain Cook's 1770 expedition.

THE LITTLE KNOWN Black Wallaroo (*Macropus bernardus*) is found in Arnhem Land in the Northern Territory (below). It is a shy animal, wary of being too close to humans.

Above: Wallaroos obtain most of their water from their food but, when there is a drought, they survive by digging holes up to a metre deep in an effort to find water.

COMMON WALLAROOS breed throughout the year. Each joey will stay in its mother's pouch for 9–12 months. Like other kangaroos, it is possible for a female wallaroo to be pregnant and have a baby in her pouch at the same time. Common Wallaroos are long-lived and, even in the wild, reach 17 or 18 years of age.

Male wallaroos stand just over 1 m tall and weigh up to 55 kg. Females are more finely built at 0.9 m and weigh 25 kg.

Left: There are four distinct types of Common Wallaroo: the Eastern Wallaroo, Northern Wallaroo, Barrow Island Wallaroo and the Euro.

Tree-kangaroos
— forest phantoms

Order: Diprotodontia
Meaning: *di* — two; *proto* — front; *dont* — tooth (two front teeth)

There are tree-dwelling animals among most groups of Australian mammals — including the phascogales, possums, Koalas, tree-rats and bats — and macropods are no exception.

the FACTS!

WHEN DISTURBED, tree-kangaroos will jump to another tree or to the ground from heights of up to 15 m.

OTHER KANGAROO SPECIES are not able to move their hindlimbs independently of each other and must move both legs together, which gives the animals their characteristic hopping gait. Tree-kangaroos are able to move their hindlimbs separately, but on the ground they still hop.

SEVERAL SMALL SPECIES of kangaroos have tails that can wrap around and carry nesting material such as grass and small branches. Tree-kangaroos are unable to grasp branches with their tails.

TREE-KANGAROOS DO NOT APPEAR to have a definite breeding season. A male will court a female by uttering a soft clucking sound and softly pawing her head and shoulders.

IT IS USUAL to find only a single tree-kangaroo species, or sometimes two, at a single locality. However, three species of tree-kangaroos do coexist in the Torricelli Mountain Range of Papua New Guinea.

TREE-KANGAROOS HAVE ADAPTED to life in the forest canopy, in much the same ways as rock-wallabies have to boulder fields and rocky outcrops. Tree-kangaroos are now confined to the rainforests of north Queensland and New Guinea, where their secretive, nocturnal lifestyle ensures they are seldom seen.

A life in the trees requires different physical skills to those of ground-dwelling animals. Tree-kangaroos have developed stronger front limbs and shorter hindlegs than other macropods and their feet have rough-textured soles for better grip on the often wet and slippery branches. Like kangaroos on the ground, a long tail is critical for maintaining balance. Despite this, tree-kangaroos are not as agile as many other arboreal mammals.

A tree-kangaroo climbs upwards by gripping the trunk or branch with its forelimbs and pushing up with the hindlimbs. When it reaches a broad horizontal branch, it will move by hopping or walking. To descend, a tree-kangaroo climbs tail first down the trunk and, on nearing the ground, it kicks off with its hindlegs to land on the forest floor.

Below: Lumholtz's Tree-kangaroo can be distinguished from the similar Bennett's Tree-kangaroo by its patterned face, pale belly and uniformly coloured tail.

AUSTRALIA HAS TWO SPECIES

of tree-kangaroo and both occur in the Wet Tropics of far north Queensland. Both are stocky animals with dense fur.

Bennett's Tree-kangaroo

(*Dendrolagus bennettianus*) is the larger of the two and is found in lowland and highland rainforests between the Daintree River and Cooktown.

Lumholtz's Tree-kangaroo

(*Dendrolagus lumholtzi*) is found mainly in higher areas of the Atherton Tableland. It has a dark face and paws and its body colouring is lighter. It is also smaller than Bennett's Tree-kangaroo.

Right: Lumholtz's Tree-kangaroo was named after the famous Norwegian naturalist and explorer, Carl Sophus Lumholtz, who worked in Australia from 1880 to 1884. He enlisted the help of Aboriginal hunters to collect specimens for him in 1882 after hearing of an unusual animal that lived high up in the rainforest.

the FACTS!

THE GESTATION PERIOD of tree-kangaroos is around 44–45 days, which is the longest of any marsupials. The female gives birth to a single joey that attaches to a teat in the pouch. Females may only raise young every second year.

SIX OF THE EIGHT living species of tree-kangaroo are found in the dense forests of New Guinea. The animal pictured below is Goodfellow's Tree-kangaroo (*Dendrolagus goodfellowi*). Logging of tropical rainforest is a major environmental problem in New Guinea. Scott's Tree-kangaroo (*Dendrolagus scottae*) and the Golden-mantled Tree-kangaroo (*Dendrolagus pulcherrimus*) are the most threatened species of tree-kangaroo in New Guinea.

IN SUITABLE HABITAT, a female Lumholtz's Tree-kangaroo will have a home territory of less than half a hectare and even the upper limit of this range is only 2.6 ha. Males are slightly more adventurous, with home ranges of 1.0–4.4 ha.

THE BLACK AND WHITE Tree-kangaroo (*Dendrolagus mbaiso*), or Dingiso, of western New Guinea was discovered quite recently and was only described as a new species in 1995. Its scientific name *mbaiso* means "forbidden". Local people regard it as a sacred animal and in some areas it is quite tame.

HIGH AND DRY

Staying dry and warm in a high rainfall region is a priority for tropical animals. A tree-kangaroo's fur is arranged so that it all points outward from about the middle of the back. This causes water to drain away from the body fur, especially when the kangaroos are sleeping. Tree-kangaroos mainly feed on leaves, but will also eat a variety of fruits.

As nocturnal animals, tree-kangaroos spend the daytime hours sleeping hunched over in a sitting position high above the ground.

Generally, tree-kangaroos are solitary animals and they are highly territorial. Their home range is usually small and they may stay within this area, even if large-scale disturbance, such as storm damage or land clearing, occurs. Forest clearing is a major threat.

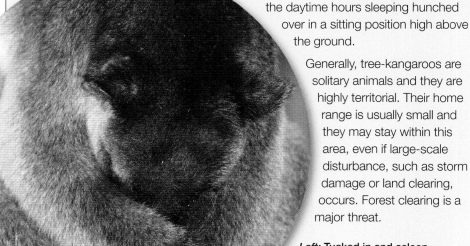

Left: Tucked in and asleep. Bennett's Tree-kangaroos have home ranges of 5.5–12.7 ha for females and 3.8–29.8 ha for males.

IAN MORRIS

Rock-wallabies
— sure-footed hoppers

Order: Diprotodontia
Meaning: *di* — two; *proto* — front; *dont* — tooth (two front teeth)

Rock-wallabies are sometimes called the "acrobats of the marsupial world" because of their ability to leap and bound over the steep and treacherous rocky habitats in which they live.

the FACTS!

THE NABARLEK (*Petrogale concinna*) is unique among all marsupials in that it can continue to produce more than the normal four molar teeth. It prefers grasses rich in silica, an abrasive mineral, and this may explain why the animal needs to continually replace its grinding teeth.

SHORT-EARED Rock-wallabies (*Petrogale brachyotis*) above, occur from the Kimberley region of Western Australia to the Queensland–Northern Territory border. They have a tuft of fur at the end of their thick tails.

HUNTING OF ROCK-WALLABIES for the fur trade no longer occurs, so several rock-wallaby groups are still recovering from population losses that occurred in the early days of European settlement.

IAN MORRIS

FEMALES, LIKE THE MAREEBA ROCK-WALLABY (*Petrogale mareeba*) below, tend to be around one-third smaller than males.

MICHAEL CERMAK

THEIR PREFERENCE for rocky areas has resulted in a diverse group of animals that vary in appearance and size. The 16 species of rock-wallaby found throughout Australia are widely separated and some are restricted to very small habitat areas.

The broken country favoured by rock-wallabies provides them with permanent waterholes and protection from summer heat and predators.

Some species leave the safety of the rocks to browse and graze on nearby slopes and terraces, but they rarely venture too far from cover. Rock-wallabies are alert and nervous and will stand and investigate noises or signs of movement, but always remain ready to quickly bound away.

Rock-wallabies eat a range of herbs, plants, young grasses and the leaves of trees. During winter they bask and feed during the day, but in summer they feed before sunrise and after sunset, spending the rest of the day in caves and under rock ledges.

Above: A Black-footed Rock-wallaby from Central Australia has left the cool shade and is sunning itself in the early morning. This is a common behaviour among rock-wallabies and particularly those whose rocky homes can drop below zero temperature at night.

Below: The Brush-tailed Rock-wallaby (*Petrogale penicillata*) is one of the darkest and plainest rock-wallabies and is found only in southern Queensland and northern New South Wales.

RIGHT: QM-BC

LIFE IN A COLONY

Rock-wallabies live in colonies. The number of animals in a colony depends on the amount of food and shelter available. In some species, little social interaction occurs between colony members, except during the breeding season and when feeding.

Female rock-wallabies can breed throughout the year, but most young are produced only when conditions are most suitable. Dominant males advertise their status by hissing, stamping and occasionally fighting.

Left: Mareeba Rock-wallabies inhabit rocky areas in dry forest and vine scrub in north-east Queensland. The fur colour of different populations tends to match the rocks where they live.

QM-BC

Above: The Black-footed Rock-wallaby (*Petrogale lateralis*) is found mainly in Central Australia and parts of Western Australia, including Barrow Island. Numbers have dramatically declined in Western Australia, mainly due to predation by feral foxes.

ROCK-WALLABIES ARE FAST, graceful macropods with an amazing ability to scale steep, slippery rock faces. They are able to achieve such feats of agility because of their powerful leg muscles and specially adapted feet. Each hindfoot has a large granular pad and a hairy fringe that serve to increase the animal's grip and prevent slippage. The wallabies also have long, slender tails that act to balance and steer the animals when moving. Rock-wallabies prefer areas with extensive rocky outcrops or boulder piles with deep fissures, caves and terraces. They tend to avoid smooth, vertical rock faces.

Left: The Proserpine Rock-wallaby (*Petrogale persephone*) has the smallest range of any rock-wallaby. It is only found in the Proserpine region of north Queensland and was only discovered in 1976. Nine of the 16 living species of rock-wallaby are found in eastern Queensland from Cape York Peninsula to near Brisbane.

Right: The Yellow-footed Rock-wallaby (*Petrogale xanthopus*) is also known as the "Ring-tailed" Rock-wallaby because of the bands on its tail. It is often considered the most beautiful of all kangaroos because of its bright colouring — fawn to grey on its back and yellow to orange on its arms, legs and feet. It also has a white cheek stripe and orange ears.

the FACTS!

THE SMALLEST rock-wallaby is the Monjon (*Petrogale burbidgei*), which is found in high rainfall areas in the Kimberley region of Western Australia. Monjons weigh only about 1–1.4 kg and are about as big as a small cat.

THE TWO LARGEST rock-wallabies are the Yellow-footed and Brush-tailed Rock-wallabies, which weigh around 11 kg, about 10 times as much as a Monjon.

Small wallabies
— down a size

Order: Diprotodontia
Meaning: *di* — two; *proto* — front; *dont* — tooth (two front teeth)

The only real difference between kangaroos and wallabies is size. The term "wallaby" is used to describe medium-sized macropods that weigh less than 25 kg. Wallabies occur throughout Australia and in all types of habitats.

the FACTS!

THE BRIDLED NAILTAIL WALLABY (above), is named for the white, crescent-shaped "bridle" line that runs down each side of its neck and shoulders. This wallaby was once common and widespread through dry country from Charters Towers in Queensland to Lake Hindmarsh in Victoria and was thought to be extinct until it was rediscovered near Dingo in central Queensland.

THE LOVELY TOOLACHE WALLABY (*Macropus greyi*) was described by early writers as the "most beautiful and elegant of all of the wallabies". However, its fine appearance resulted in the animal being hunted ruthlessly for sport, bounties and skins. The last wild Toolache were recorded in 1924, and with the death of the last captives around 1937, the Toolache became extinct.

THE AGILE WALLABY (*Macropus agilis*) is the most common wallaby in tropical northern Australia.

Above: The Western Brush Wallaby (*Macropus irma*) is also known as the Black-gloved Wallaby because of its distinctive black paws.

WALLABIES CAN BE GROUPED according to how similar they are to larger kangaroos. Eight species are so closely related that they are even placed in the same genus as the kangaroo — *Macropus*.

Four other species are less closely related, although the differences are minor. These include the swamp wallabies (*Wallabia*) and the nailtail wallabies (*Onychogalea*).

SIMILAR, BUT DIFFERENT

One of the few points of difference between wallabies and kangaroos is their colour pattern. In general, kangaroos tend to be quite plain, but many wallabies have bright cheek, ear and hip stripes. In some species, such as the Whiptail Wallaby (*Macropus parryi*), these markings are very prominent. Whiptail Wallabies are commonly known as "Pretty-face" Wallabies because of their bright facial markings.

Left: Whiptail Wallabies live in mobs of up to 50 animals. Within the mob, there are subgroups of up to 10 adults and young.

Conservation Watch

Two species of wallaby are Extinct.
The Bridled Nailtail Wallaby is Endangered.

The Swamp Wallaby is common throughout eastern Queensland, New South Wales, Victoria and south-eastern South Australia.

The milk of the Tammar Wallaby (*Macropus eugenii*) contains an antibacterial component thought to be 100 times more powerful than penicillin.

Parma Wallabies (*Macropus parma*) were thought to be extinct until small numbers were found in the wild and a feral population was identified near Auckland in New Zealand.

WHEN EUROPEAN SETTLERS first arrived in Australia, they found more species of macropods than exist today. Loss of habitat, grazing, feral animals and hunting all took a toll on macropods. The large kangaroos not only survived; some are even thriving. The same is not true of wallabies and small macropods, which proved to be very vulnerable to all threats.

NAILTAIL WALLABIES

Nailtail wallabies are named for the horny spur on the tip of their tails. The purpose of the nail is unknown. Nailtails are shy, solitary animals that feed on grasses and leaves. They begin feeding at dusk and continue into the night. During the day, the wallabies rest in a shallow scrape made in a shady spot.

The three species of nailtail wallabies are: the Crescent Nailtail Wallaby (*Onychogalea lunata*), which is now extinct; the Bridled Nailtail Wallaby (*Onychogalea fraenata*), which survives only in a small area around Dingo in Queensland; and the Northern Nailtail (*Onychogalea unguifera*), which is common across northern Australia.

The Northern Nailtail Wallaby is the largest of the three nailtails. Its sandy colour gave rise to its other common name, the Sandy Nailtail Wallaby.

SWAMP WALLABY

The Swamp Wallaby (*Wallabia bicolor*) is a small, stocky wallaby with dark brown fur, often with lighter rusty patches on the belly, chest and base of the ears (right). It prefers heath, woodland and forest with undergrowth, where it feeds on a variety of plants, including native and introduced shrubs, grasses and ferns.

Far right: The Golden Swamp Wallaby (*Wallabia bicolor welsbyi*) is named for its beautiful gold to rusty-coloured fur. It occurs only on North and South Stradbroke Islands in southern Queensland.

the FACTS!

WALLABIES RANGE IN SIZE from the little Parma Wallaby (*Macropus parma*), which weighs only 3 to 6 kg, to the large male Red-necked Wallaby (*Macropus rufogriseus*), at 27 kg.

THE RED-NECKED WALLABY (*Macropus rufogriseus*) was one of the first marsupials observed and reported from Port Jackson after the arrival of the First Fleet.

Pademelons
— smaller still

Order: Diprotodontia
Meaning: *di* — two; *proto* — front; *dont* — tooth (two front teeth)

Pademelons are small, compact, knee-high wallabies with short tails and legs. They are creatures of the forest and are often heard thumping and then hopping away from walking tracks and nature trails.

OCCASIONALLY, PADEMELONS will venture to the edge of picnic grounds in national parks to browse on grasses, but for most of the day they stay hidden among the forest undergrowth. When alarmed, they thump their hindfeet to warn companions. Their small size and reddish-brown colour make them difficult to see.

the FACTS!

LITTLE IS KNOWN about the breeding biology of the Red-legged Pademelon, but it feeds on a variety of fruits, leaves, grasses and fungi. It sleeps from midmorning to midafternoon with its back against a tree or rock and its head tucked forwards onto its tail.

RED-NECKED PADEMELONS browse on herbs and soft-leaved shrubs. They are usually solitary animals, but small groups may gather for feeding and breeding. These pademelons reach maturity at around 18 months. Their breeding season is mid to late summer.

ALTHOUGH IT BECAME EXTINCT on mainland Australia more than 100 years ago, the Rufous-bellied Pademelon still occurs in Tasmania, where it is so abundant that limited hunting is allowed. Its fur and meat are both commercially valuable. In the wild, pademelons live about four to six years.

Above: The Red-legged Pademelon occurs along the tropical and subtropical east coast of Australia and in New Guinea. It rarely ventures far from its forest home.

PADEMELONS EAT JUICY GRASSES and shrubs and they make well-travelled tracks ("runways") through ground vegetation between their shelter and feeding areas. Males are larger than females and pademelons breed once a year, raising a single young.

Three species of pademelon — the Red-legged (*Thylogale stigmatica*), the Red-necked (*Thylogale thetis*) and the Rufous-bellied Pademelon (*Thylogale billardierii*) — live in the rainforests and wet eucalypt forests of eastern Australia, as far south as Tasmania.

Left: The Rufous-bellied Pademelon is known for its fine fur and it was once hunted in great numbers.

Quokkas
— island charmers

Order: Diprotodontia
Meaning: *di* — two; *proto* — front; *dont* — tooth (two front teeth)

The Quokka (Setonix brachyurus) is probably the best known inhabitant of Rottnest Island, in Western Australia, where it has become a tourist attraction. It is also found in bushland around the capital of Western Australia, Perth.

ROTTNEST ISLAND IS A POPULAR HOLIDAY SPOT and, because of the Quokka's long, close contact with island visitors, they have become more friendly and approachable than wild animals would usually be.

Quokkas are small wallabies that grow to the size of a hare or domestic cat. They congregate under dense shrubs for shelter and are less active during the day. At night, they feed on grasses, leaves, bark and succulent plants.

Quokkas breed all year round. Joeys are born after a gestation period of four months and a young animal will live in its mother's pouch for the first 25 weeks of its life. It reaches maturity at about one and a half to two years. Quokkas are long-lived and can reach 10 years of age.

Above: Quokkas are extremely adaptable animals. If there is no fresh water in summer, they are able to obtain water from plants and they can exist for long periods of time without drinking.

the FACTS!

"QUOKKA" IS THE NAME GIVEN to the animal by the Aboriginal people living in the Augusta and King George Sound area of Western Australia.

IN 1696, the Dutch explorer Willem de Vlamingh described the Quokka as "a kind of rat as big as a common cat". He named the island where he saw them, "Rotte nest" (meaning "rat's nest") Island.

QUOKKAS RECYCLE a small amount of their body waste products.

VISITORS TO ROTTNEST ISLAND must not feed the Quokkas, as the animals may become ill after eating unsuitable food, such as bread, chips and meat.

BY THE 1960s, mainland Quokkas had declined to no more than a few populations around Perth. Fortunately, careful preservation of habitat and baiting of introduced predators has led to a recovery. Quokkas are now locally common in parts of south-west Western Australia.

A HARSH ISLAND HOME

Rottnest Island is a harsh environment. Young Quokkas suffer from anaemia, a sometimes fatal illness caused by the low nitrogen content of local plants in summer and insufficient water. Quokkas can also be deficient in the important trace elements of cobalt and copper, which are scarce in Rottnest Island soils. Copper levels may influence when and how the animals breed.

Despite this, the Quokka is still relatively common, although not as widespread as it was before European settlement. It is believed that the number of Quokkas on Rottnest Island averages about 10,000, at a density of five animals per hectare, and that the population fluctuates from 4000 to 17,000, depending on the availability of food and water in any given year.

Above: Quokkas are grizzled brown in colour with rufous (reddish) cheeks, ears, neck and shoulders. The belly colour is buff.

Conservation Watch

Two species are Extinct. Two species are Endangered. Threats include changes to habitat and predation by feral animals.

Hare-wallabies
— pocket macropods

Order: Diprotodontia
Meaning: *di* — two; *proto* — front; *dont* — tooth (two front teeth)

Early European settlers thought that "hare" wallabies resembled hares, which are not marsupials. Both groups of animals are similar in size and agility and both have the same habit of hiding in clumps of grass.

the FACTS!

ALTHOUGH THEY ARE MATURE at one year old, hare-wallabies do not usually breed until their second year. The mating season is long, beginning in December and ending in September the following year. Gestation appears to last for several months and mothers usually raise only one young each year.

IF HARE-WALLABIES ARE DISTURBED, they burst from their shelter and run swiftly in a zig-zag manner to escape. They often make a high-pitched squeak as they run.

EARLY NATURALIST JOHN GOULD was particularly impressed by the jumping ability of a hare-wallaby that was chased by his dogs in South Australia during the 1840s. He wrote: "The animal had arrived within 20 feet before it observed me, when ... instead of branching off to the right or left; it bounded clear over my head."

THE FIRST SPECIMENS of the Banded Hare-wallaby (*Lagostrophus fasciatus*) were collected in 1801. The wallaby may be the last survivor of an ancient group of macropods known as Sthenurines, or "short-faced kangaroos", which became extinct about 18,000 years ago.

THE HARE-WALLABIES are nocturnal and live in dry forests, woodlands, shrublands and hummock grasslands. They nest in thickets and spend the day in squats, or short burrows, under grass tussocks or low shrubs. Most species are solitary and only come together to feed. Deeper burrows (up to 700 mm deep) may be cooler than surface temperatures.

Their diet of grasses, fruit, herbs and seeds provides most of the water the wallabies need. Males always behave aggressively towards other males when competing for food, but they are not hostile towards females.

When Europeans came to Australia 200 years ago, five species of hare-wallaby ranged across the mainland and some offshore islands. Only one, the Spectacled Hare-wallaby (*Lagorchestes conspicillatus*), remains widespread.

Above: Wildfires, drought and foxes have caused the Rufous Hare-wallaby (*Lagorchestes hirsutus*), or Mala, to become extinct in Central Australia. Malas are able to eat hardy spinifex grass to survive, but prefer more succulent plants.

SURVIVING IN THE TROPICS

Populations of Spectacled Hare-wallabies have declined across Australia in the past 100 years, but it has fared better than others. Its survival is probably due to the fact that the wallaby also inhabits tropical areas, where land clearing, fire patterns and grazing by introduced animals has not been as severe as in arid regions.

Other species of hare-wallabies have been protected on offshore islands that are free of introduced predators. The Banded Hare-wallaby (left) is now being reintroduced into protected mainland reserves.

The Spectacled Hare-wallaby (right) can conserve water by producing highly concentrated urine. They also have a low metabolic rate.

Bettongs
— distant relatives

Order: Diprotodontia
Meaning: *di* — two; *proto* — front; *dont* — tooth (two front teeth)

At first glance, bettongs look very similar to hare-wallabies, but they are only distantly related to macropods and have their own special characteristics. The closest relatives of bettongs are potoroos and Desert Rat-kangaroos.

BETTONGS ARE FOUND in grassy open forests and woodlands. They are active at night, avoiding activity in the moisture-losing heat of the day when they shelter in burrows, vegetation or nests.

Unlike small macropods, bettongs do not graze and browse; instead they dig for fungi, tubers and roots. This diet explains why bettongs and macropods have different types of teeth.

Most do not drink except during drought. They satisfy their water needs from the plants they eat and their diet also includes grasses, seeds, bulbs, lilies and insects. Underground "truffle" fungi are a favourite.

In the wild, bettongs live for three to five years. If conditions are suitable, they are able to breed throughout the year. Young are born 21 days after mating and up to three young can be raised each year.

Left: The Burrowing Bettong (*Bettongia lesueur*) is the only species of bettong that constructs burrows. Upwards of 50 Burrowing Bettongs will live in the same warrens and a single warren may have several entrances.

the FACTS!

EVEN THOUGH THEY ARE SMALL animals, some bettongs may travel up to 4.5 km from their nests to suitable feeding areas.

ALL BETTONGS CARRY NESTING MATERIAL by curling their semi-prehensile tails around bundles of grass and fibre. Young Rufous Bettongs (below) live in the pouch about 3.5 months and are weaned at 5–6 months.

THE NORTHERN BETTONG (*Bettongia tropica*) is found in high areas with less fertile soils, usually about 400m above sea level. The fungi that are an important part of its diet are most abundant in poor soils, so this may explain the choice of habitat.

BURROWING BETTONGS are fond of figs and will build their warrens under a fig tree if possible. They will also occasionally eat carrion found on beaches.

BETTONGS AND THE RELATED POTOROOS have sacs in their forestomachs. These contain bacteria that help break down plant material.

BRUSH-TAILED BETTONGS (*Bettongia penicillata*) have been bred in captivity and released on islands off the coast of South Australia.

Above: The Rufous Bettong (*Aepyprymnus rufescens*) along with the Southern Bettong (*Bettongia gaimardi*) are the only species that can be regarded as common. Even so, land clearing has severely reduced their original habitat.

Conservation Watch
One species is Extinct. Two species are Endangered. Threats include habitat loss, feral herbivores, fire and feral predators.

Potoroos
— a taste for truffles

Order: Diprotodontia
Meaning: *di* — two; *proto* — front; *dont* — tooth (two front teeth)

Potoroos look like a cross between a small macropod and a bandicoot. They have pointed faces like bandicoots, but also have the short "arms", long hindfeet and the hopping gait of kangaroos.

the FACTS!

POTOROOS ARE NOCTURNAL and during the day rest in bowl-shaped depressions and squats hidden by shrubs, grasses and sedges. They feed in the open, often along forest edges, but quickly retreat to thick undergrowth for protection.

AUSTRALIA HAS ABOUT 1200 species of native "truffle" fungi and many species exude a strong odour to attract animals like potoroos and bandicoots. In this way, the fungi spores are spread to new areas through animal droppings.

THE LONG-FOOTED POTOROO (below) was only discovered in 1968, but it was not recognised as a separate species until a decade later.

POTOROOS ARE MAINLY FOUND in the wet forests and heathlands of eastern and southern Australia, but two species also occur in the south-west corner of Western Australia. One of these, Gilbert's Potoroo (*Potorous gilbertii*), is Australia's most endangered mammal.

Right: The Long-nosed Potoroo is found from South-East Queensland to Tasmania and is vulnerable nationally.

POTOROOS LEAVE SMALL diggings in the soil similar to those of bandicoots.

IT IS BELIEVED that only about 30 individuals of Gilbert's Potoroo exist in the wild. Captive breeding programs are under way in the attempt to save the potoroo.

A TASTE FOR TRUFFLES

Potoroos are "addicted" to fungi, in particular to the underground fruiting bodies known as "truffles". Truffles make up more than 90 per cent of the diet of Gilbert's Potoroo (left) making it one of the most fungi-dependent mammals in the world.

Similarly, the Long-nosed Potoroo (*Potorous tridactylus*) eats more than 40 species, while the Long-footed Potoroo (*Potorous longipes*), which is restricted to East Gippsland in Victoria, munches through at least 33 species.

Potoroos have long curved claws on their forefeet, which are ideal for digging up truffles. Most types eaten by the potoroo are only about 10 cm beneath the soil.

Rat-kangaroos
— a world apart

Order: Diprotodontia
Meaning: *di* — two; *proto* — front; *dont* — tooth (two front teeth)

"Rat-kangaroo" or "kangaroo-rat" is a term often used to describe small hopping animals. However, only two Australian mammals are officially known as "rat-kangaroos" and although they share a similar name, they are very different.

THE MUSKY RAT-KANGAROO (*Hypsiprymnodon moschatus*) is the smallest member of the kangaroo family and is about the size of a large guinea pig. It is found only in Tropical North Queensland and prefers the wettest parts of the rainforest, where it feeds on fallen fruits, as well as fungi, earthworms, grasshoppers and other small invertebrate animals. Near the end of the fruiting season, the Musky Rat-kangaroo collects fruit to bury beneath the leaf litter. This is known as "scatter-hoarding" or "caching" and the food is retrieved during lean times. The Musky Rat-kangaroo is the only Australian marsupial known to scatter-hoard.

Above: The dark brown Musky Rat-kangaroo is similar in shape, size and habit to *Hypsiprymnodon bartholomai*, a small animal that lived during the mid-Miocene Period, about 15 million years ago.

GRASS NESTS IN A DRY, HOT ENVIRONMENT

The Desert Rat-kangaroo (*Caloprymnus campestris*) was a desert-dweller that once ranged over the sand ridges, gibber plains and claypans of south-west Queensland and parts of South Australia. This is some of the hottest, driest and most exposed country in Australia.

Desert Rat-kangaroos sheltered in a flimsy, grass nest placed under a small bush or out in the open. Each nest was occupied by only one adult and individuals foraged separately. Unfortunately, the grass nests provided no protection against hooved animals or feral predators.

Left: The Desert Rat-kangaroo was discovered in the 1840s and then not seen for 90 years; it reappeared in 1931 and then suddenly declined to extinction.

the FACTS!

UNLIKE OTHER KANGAROO species, which feed at dusk and dawn, the Musky Rat-kangaroo is diurnal, gathering food, like quandong fruit (below), during the day. The kangaroos have prehensile tails, similar to possums, and use their tails to carry nesting material and to help them climb over low branches on the forest floor.

MUSKY RAT-KANGAROOS are the only macropods to regularly give birth to more than one young at a time. It is not uncommon for females to have two or three babies, which stay in their mother's pouch for about 21 weeks. When they are a little older, the young leave their nest on the forest floor and accompany the female on her search for food.

ALTHOUGH IT WAS FIRST described by scientists in 1875, little was known about the biology of the Musky Rat-kangaroo until recent times.

MUSKY RAT-KANGAROOS do not hop like other macropods, but scurry along on all fours. They also have a thumb-like toe on each hindfoot.

THE LAST RECORD of the Desert Rat-kangaroo was made in 1935 at Ooroowilanie, east of Lake Eyre in South Australia. The animal was known for its speed and endurance. Bush folklore said that, when chased, it could elude both man and horse.

MICHAEL CERMAK

Megabats
— flighty campers

Order: Chiroptera
Meaning: *chiro* — hand; *ptera* — wing (hand-wings)

the FACTS!

THE ORIGIN OF BATS is uncertain, but they may have evolved from a single, shrew-like ancestor that was able to glide.

BAT FOSSILS FROM 50 MILLION years ago have been discovered at Murgon in Queensland and at other places around the world. Modern bats have changed very little from their ancient ancestors.

SOME LITTLE RED FLYING-FOX camps may number up to one million individuals.

THE BLACK FLYING-FOX (*Pteropus alecto*), is one of the world's largest bats, with a wingspan of more than 1m (below). It is occasionally seen electrocuted on powerlines. Recently, Black Flying-foxes have been seen in Sydney.

IAN MORRIS

FLY-OUTS OF HUNDREDS and sometimes thousands of Black Flying-foxes, leaving their daytime roosts, are a common sight in evening skies across northern Australia. The fly-outs can change direction nightly, the bats often following watercourses in a keen search for food.

QM-GC

Above: Little Red Flying-foxes (*Pteropus scapulatus*) are highly nomadic creatures. They move camp every one to two months to follow flowering trees.

Bats are the only group of mammals that can fly. Their wings are formed by a skin membrane that is stretched over elongated fingers and forearms and extends from the shoulders, along the sides of the body to the ankles. Bats also have lightweight skeletons compared to similar-sized mammals.

THERE ARE TWO TYPES OF BATS, each with a very different lifestyle. The "megabats" are the flying-foxes and their relatives. Flying-foxes are fruit and nectar feeders ranging in size from tiny blossom-bats to larger animals with wingspans of more than 1 m. "Microbats" are generally much smaller in size (up to 30 cm wingspans), and feed mainly on insects and other animals.

FLYING-FOXES

Flying-foxes have good night vision and an excellent sense of smell to help them navigate through the darkness and locate food. They also have highly developed memories to assist them in finding feeding sites and roosts they have previously visited.

Noisy bat colonies, or "camps", numbering from a dozen to thousands of animals, can be found in many parts of Australia, particularly near waterways and in coastal areas. In the largest camps, roost trees may bend and break under the weight of the bats.

Right: The Grey-headed Flying-fox (*Pteropus poliocephalus*) is the only flying-fox that lives and breeds in southern Australia. It is sometimes found on the Bass Strait islands. Little Red Flying-foxes are occasional visitors to Victoria and South Australia.

LEFT & CENTRE: LES HALL; RIGHT: QM

FRIENDS OF THE FOREST

Flying-foxes need access to flowering and fruiting trees to sustain their large colonies. They leave their roosts at dusk and may fly up to 50 km in a night to feeding sites.

The bats are important pollinators of native plants. In their travels, flying-foxes disperse seeds in their droppings and carry a dusting of pollen from tree to tree, fertilising flowers as they feed. Eucalypt trees rely heavily on the bats, producing most of their nectar and pollen at night to coincide with the bats' feeding times.

Flying-foxes also eat cultivated fruit and may be nuisances around backyards and orchards. Half-eaten fruit, small pellets of mouthed fruit pulp, broken off sprigs of eucalypt flowers and pasty droppings are all signs of flying-fox feeding areas.

Unfortunately, conflicts with humans are increasing as urban development and farms replace what was once flying-fox habitat.

QM

Above right: Eastern Blossom-bats (*Syconycteris australis*) live in heathland, swamps and forests along the coast of eastern Queensland and northern New South Wales.

THE LITTLE MEGABATS

JACK PETTIGREW

The flying-fox family includes the blossom-bats (two species) and tube-nosed bats. Unlike their larger cousins, small megabats are solitary or live in small groups.

Tiny blossom-bats are mainly nectar feeders, while tube-nosed bats prefer fruit, but will take some nectar and pollen as well. Tube-nosed bats are extremely agile in flight and can hover easily.

These small megabats roost in the canopy of rainforest trees. Northern Blossom-bats (*Macroglossus minimus*) also shelter under bark and at the opening of tree hollows.

Above: Eastern Tube-nosed Bat (*Nyctimene robinsoni*) has yellow spots on ears and nostrils. The function of the oddly shaped nostrils of the tube-nosed bat is still unknown.

the FACTS!

THE LITTLE RED FLYING-FOX is capable of crossing the Tasman Sea if conditions are favourable. There are reports from as early as 1854 of "large bats" being seen in New Zealand, but the first confirmed record occurred in 1927–29, when a dead animal was found on the North Island.

THE SPECTACLED FLYING-FOX (*Pteropus conspicillatus*) always camps near rainforest and is known to disperse the seeds of at least 26 species of rainforest canopy tree.

THE MOUSE-SIZED Eastern Blossom-bat (below) is the smallest Australian megabat and an important pollinator of native plants. Its diet varies according to where it lives. In the tropical north the bats eat fruit, nectar, pollen and some leaves from rainforest trees. In the cooler south, their diet is almost exclusively nectar and pollen from heathland plants such as banksias.

LES HALL

THE EASTERN TUBE-NOSED BAT roosts alone and, with its wings folded, resembles a large dead leaf. The bat inhabits forests, woodlands and heaths in eastern Queensland and northern New South Wales. Its call is a high-pitched whistling bleat.

Microbats
— pulses in the dark

Order: Chiroptera
Meaning: *chiro* — hand; *ptera* — wing (hand-wings)

Microbats differ from megabats because they use high-frequency sound, rather than sight and smell, to navigate in the dark and to find food. Each bat emits pulses of ultrasonic soundwaves through its mouth and then listens for faint echoes of these pulses as the sound reflects off its surroundings.

the FACTS!

SHEATHTAIL-BATS have mouse-like faces and they are usually brown, rufous or golden-brown. The Yellow-bellied Sheathtail-bat (*Saccolaimus flaviventris*) is an exception. It is black with a white or cream belly.

THE FLIGHT MEMBRANE of microbats also extends between the hindlegs and is used as a rudder and, sometimes, as a scoop to help catch prey.

GOULD'S LONG-EARED BAT (*Nyctophilus gouldi*) below, hunts around houses and in orchards for insect pests. The bat changes its roost site regularly and will readily use artificial bat boxes.

Below: Gould's Wattled Bats (*Chalinolobus gouldii*) emit chirps when flying, chitter when roosting, and squeak, chirp and make low buzzing noises if handled.

THE ECHOES allow the bat to "map" its surroundings by judging the distance, size and location of prey animals or obstacles. The frequency and style of echolocation calls varies from species to species and depends on the bat's flight speed, wing design, diet and the type of habitat in which it lives or hunts.

Analysis of sound pulses is an important tool used by scientists to identify different species of bat. The bizarre faces, folded noses and shell-like ears of some microbats help them to focus the pulses and echoes.

Right: The Eastern Horseshoe-bat (*Rhinolophus megaphyllus*) enters houses to chase prey and sometimes uses verandahs as a night roost while feeding.

Above: Coastal Sheathtail-bats (*Taphozous australis*) roost in sea caves, rock fissures and old bunkers near the ocean. They hunt beetles and other insects at nightfall.

THEIR ECHOLOCATION SKILLS make microbats very effective predators that catch as much as 90 per cent of all the prey they attack. However, some insects can detect bat sonar and are able to take evasive action.

Microbats normally roost in caves, in the hollows of living or dead trees, or under bark. They also roost in the roof or wall cavities of buildings and in stormwater drains and other built structures.

Colonies range in size from a few individuals to many thousands of animals, as in the case of the Common Bentwing Bat (*Miniopterus schreibersii*). During the breeding season, females congregate in maternity roosts.

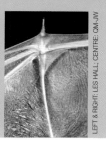

Conservation Watch

One species is Critically Endangered. One species is Endangered. Two subspecies are Vulnerable. Another subspecies is At Risk.

MORE THAN 60 SPECIES OF MICROBAT, belonging to six families, occur in Australia. They vary in size and form, but most are 7–15 cm long and weigh less than 100 g.

Horseshoe-bats have large ears and a wrinkled, horseshoe-shaped "noseleaf". They roost in warm humid caves, holes, rock crevices, old mines, tunnels and buildings.

A leafnosed-bat looks very similar to a horseshoe-bat, but the folds of skin on its nose are not as fleshy. The bats hunt flying insects near the ground or around foliage, and they are also able to hover when seeking prey.

Right: Dusky Leafnosed-bats (*Hipposideros ater*) occur across tropical northern Australia. They have a slow, highly manoeuvrable flight, which is suitable for hunting in dense vegetation, such as mangroves and rainforest. They roost in caves, old mines and tree hollows.

ORDINARY BATS

Ordinary bats are the most numerous and widespread group of bats in Australia. Most ordinary bats have small eyes, a small flap of skin called the "tragus" in the ear, and domed heads.

The 36 species of ordinary bats differ in their behaviour and their ecology. They roost in a variety of sites and may be solitary animals or may form colonies. Some ordinary bats hibernate, while others are migratory.

Most species of ordinary bats feed on flying insects and may consume up to half their body weight in insects every night, but others are specialist feeders. The Large-footed Myotis (*Myotis macropus*) is known as Australia's "fishing bat" because it catches small fish and aquatic insects by skimming its long toes over the surface of water. The Golden-tipped Bat (*Kerivoula papuensis*) feeds on orb-weaving spiders that it plucks from their webs.

Left: The Eastern Broad-nosed Bat (*Scotorepens orion*) with young.

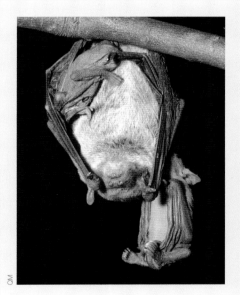

SHEATHTAIL-BATS LIVE IN TREE HOLLOWS, caves and crevices. They are fast, agile hunters and most of their flying insect prey is eaten on the wing. The lower half of the tail is enclosed by the tail membrane.

A FREETAIL-BAT has wrinkled lips and its tail protrudes from the end of the tail membrane. Freetails roost in tree hollows, under loose bark, in dead stumps and in building cavities. Large colonies may number several hundred individuals.

the FACTS!

BATS ARE NOT THE ONLY terrestrial mammals that echolocate: some ground-dwelling shrews, a small mammal from Europe, can echolocate as well.

A MICROBAT CAN JUDGE its altitude using sonar returns from the ground.

Ghost Bats
— false vampires

Order: Chiroptera
Meaning: *chiro* — hand; *ptera* — wing (hand-wings)

Bats feature in supernatural tales and folklore and, as a result, they have an undeserved reputation as frightening creatures. In earlier times, the ethereal Ghost Bat and similar species of microbats, were often called "vampire bats" because it was mistakenly believed that they drank the blood of their prey.

the FACTS!

GHOST BATS HAVE A LONG FOSSIL HISTORY in Australia. Not only were they much more widely distributed in the past, there were also more species of ghost bats.

THE DOMAIN OF THE GHOST BAT includes rainforest, vine scrub, forest and woodlands across northern Australia from the arid Pilbara region of northern Western Australia to high-rainfall areas of eastern Queensland.

GHOST BATS ARE KNOWN TO PREY on more than 50 species of bird. They prefer small species and those that cluster together when roosting. Most of the birds taken by Ghost Bats weigh less than 35 g.

GHOST BATS ECHOLOCATE using low-intensity calls that are difficult to detect with bat detectors. They also make distinctive twitters and chirps when roosting and foraging.

IAN MORRIS

Above: The Ghost Bat is the world's second-largest microbat, with a 60 cm wingspan. It is also one of the few bats with light-coloured or white fur.

IN FACT, THE GHOST BAT (*Macroderma gigas*) prefers meat to blood and is Australia's only bat that is truly carnivorous, preying on other bats, small mammals, birds, frogs and also large insects. Like other microbats, they scan for prey using echolocation, but they also have excellent vision and hearing.

A STEALTHY HUNTER

Much of a Ghost Bat's prey is captured on the ground. The bats fly above the ground, or hang from vantage points up to 3 m high. When perched, the bats constantly move their heads and twitch their ears as they scan.

If it senses a prey animal, a Ghost Bat will swoop down, wrap its wings around the prey and kill it with a powerful bite. The prey is then taken away to a feeding site to be eaten. The less palatable portions of the prey are discarded. Accumulations of remains are a good indication of the presence of Ghost Bats.

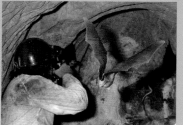

Conservation Watch

Secure but some populations are At Risk. Threats include disturbance and loss of roosts, habitat changes and feral predators. Barbed-wire fences are also a serious threat.

NOT SO "SPOOKY"

Ghost bats are named for their pale-grey, brown or whitish fur and wing membranes. In some circumstances, the bats' wings appear almost translucent and this adds to their "spooky" image. Ghost Bats also have very large ears, which are joined above the head, large eyes and a long noseleaf, but no tail. They weigh 140–165 g.

Although the Ghost Bat is Australia's largest and heaviest microbat, it is still not as big as the smallest flying-fox, the Torresian Flying-fox (*Pteropus banakrisi*), which is 160–200 mm long and weighs 210–240 g.

the FACTS!

CLIMATE CHANGE may be affecting the distribution of Ghost Bats, as their range appears to be shrinking. They are now found in areas up to 400 km inland, but until recently they extended much further inland and further south.

THERE REALLY ARE "VAMPIRE" BATS that feed on the blood of large mammals. The Common Vampire Bat (*Desmodus rotundus*) from Central and South America and two related species from South America make small cuts in the skin of their prey and lap up the pooling blood.

GHOST BATS ARE LOW-ENERGY HUNTERS. They remain stationary at a vantage-point and make only short flights to capture slow-flying insects and animals on the ground. Other microbats expend more energy because they actively pursue their prey through the air.

ROOSTING AND BREEDING

Ghost Bats roost in caves, deep rock crevices, overhangs and old mines. Their colonies range in size from a few individuals to hundreds of bats. Large colonies of up to 1000 bats are known, but these are very rare.

Some roosts are used as shelters and others for raising young. Ghost Bat populations are centred on the "maternity" or "nursery" roosts, but in all of Australia, only ten such sites are known to exist. There may be more large roosts still to be discovered in remote areas.

Male and female Ghost Bats live in separate colonies during the breeding season, which begins in winter. Females give birth to one live young the following spring.

Young bats are born helpless and hairless. They feed on milk from teats located under their mothers' armpits, until they are weaned on prey, which their mothers bring to the roost. Juvenile Ghost Bats hunt with their mothers until they are able to look for prey themselves.

SIMILAR "FALSE VAMPIRE" BATS are found in Africa, India and South-East Asia. These bats are called "false vampires" because they lack the front biting teeth (incisors) of true vampire bats.

Native rats
— a curious assortment

Order: Rodentia
Meaning: *rodens* — gnaw (gnawers)

Rats and mice belong to the largest and most diverse group of mammals — the rodents. Unfortunately, rodents have a bad reputation — thanks to a few feral pest species.

AUSTRALIA'S 64 SPECIES of native rats and mice are shy, secretive creatures that are difficult to tell apart from their introduced relatives and small marsupials.

Rodents have a pair of long incisor teeth at the tip of the mouth on the upper and lower jaws. The mouth of a marsupial is either full of tiny sharp teeth, like a dog or cat, or has multiple upper incisors.

the FACTS!

RODENTS HAVE CONSTANTLY GROWING INCISORS that must be kept "trimmed" by gnawing on hard objects such as wood, nut shells and hard seeds.

A SWIMMING WATER-RAT (below) can be easily mistaken for a Platypus because of its smooth shiny fur and streamlined body. The Water-rat, which grows to nearly 40 cm long and weighs up to 1.2 kg, is found over much of northern, eastern, southern and south-western Australia.

THE LONG-HAIRED RAT of inland Australia goes through cycles of abundance and scarcity. "Plagues" of these rats occur after heavy rainfall, when food is readily available. As the food supply dwindles, the rats die off.

THE CANEFIELD RAT (*Rattus sordidus*) is one of several rodent species that is a pest in the canefields of eastern Queensland.

WATER-RATS FEED along the water's edge, where they leave piles ("middens") of inedible prey remains, such as mussel shells and crayfish claws.

Above: The Tree Mouse was thought to be rare until scientists working at night found them to be quite common in the canopy of rainforests.

Above: Coconuts are a favourite food of the Giant White-tailed Rat, which nests in tree hollows in tropical rainforests. These rats also cache seeds.

TYPICAL RATS

Rats are generally thought of as small, solidly built mammals, with naked scaly tails, that scurry around at ground level (or sometimes in trees). The Broad-toothed Rat (*Mastacomys fuscus*) and the seven other native *Rattus* species certainly look like this, although none are climbers. Native rats occur mostly in higher rainfall regions in northern, eastern and southern Australia. The only inland species, the Long-haired Rat (*Rattus villosissimus*), survives by hiding in soil crevices. They make nests of shredded grass.

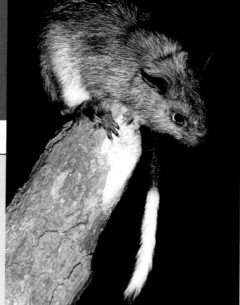

Conservation Watch

Eight species are Extinct; two are Endangered and three are Vulnerable.

Above: Ponds surrounded by dead fish, feeding "tables" scattered with shells and other leftovers, and a strong fishy scent, are all sure signs of Water-rat activity.

Above: The shaggy-coated, rare Black-footed Tree-rat (*Mesembriomys gouldii*) is huge — weighing 880 g. It lives in tropical areas from Western Australia to the Northern Territory and north Queensland.

the FACTS!

A RODENT'S INCISORS can be used as a multipurpose tool: as delicate forceps for grooming and food manipulation; as chisels for gnawing; or as biting weapons in attack and defence.

THE CENTRAL ROCK-RAT (*Zyzomys pendunculatus*) was thought to be extinct until it was rediscovered in the West MacDonnell Ranges in 1996.

STICK-NEST RATS feed on the leaves and stems of succulent plants, as well as some seeds.

THE WATER-RATS

Water-rats (*Hydromys chrysogaster*) are good swimmers and will dive for food. They eat crayfish, mussels, frogs, fish, lizards and small birds and can be seen at any time during the day, but are most active around dusk. When they are not searching for food, Water-rats shelter in hollow logs or burrows excavated in creek banks.

THE TREE-RATS

Most of Australia's tree-rats are confined to the tropical north of the country. They have an arboreal lifestyle, feeding on seeds, fruit, nectar, insects and green tips. The Giant White-tailed Rat (*Uromys caudimaculatus*), from Queensland's Wet Tropics, also preys on bird eggs and nestlings.

THE STICK-NEST RATS

A nest built of woven sticks gave the stick-nest rats (*Leporillus* species) their common name. Their nests are usually found under bushes, rock overhangs and in caves in the drier parts of Australia. At the time of European settlement there were two species, but the Greater Stick-nest Rat (*Leporillus conditor*) is the only one that survives.

THE ROCK-RATS

Rocky habitats provide excellent homes for wildlife so it is not surprising to find a group of Australian rodents that has adapted to this environment. Rock-rats (*Zyzomys* species) occur across tropical northern and eastern Australia, but usually only in small, isolated populations. The one exception is the Common Rock-rat (*Zyzomys argurus*) that can be found from Western Australia to Queensland.

Above: Bush Rats (*Rattus fuscipes*) occur in coastal and montane forests of eastern and southern Australia. These rats have a varied diet, but eat more insects than other native rats.

Native mice
— bounders to builders

Order: Rodentia
Meaning: *rodens* — gnaw (gnawers)

the FACTS!

THE DARLING DOWNS HOPPING-MOUSE (*Notomys mordax*) is known only from a single skull collected somewhere on the Darling Downs of southern Queensland in the 1840s. There have been no further sightings of this animal.

PERHAPS THE MOST ENDANGERED Australian rodent is the Bramble Cay Melomys (*Melomys rubicola*). It lives on a single vegetated coral cay at the northern tip of the Great Barrier Reef. The cay, which measures 340 m long by 150 m wide, is shrinking because it is being eroded by waves.

A 12 G PEBBLE-MOUND MOUSE is capable of lifting a rock double its size — with its mouth!

IT IS NOT KNOWN why pebble-mound mice build their amazing mounds, but it is thought that they provide cool shelters from high day-time temperatures.

THE BLUE-GREY MOUSE (*Pseudomys glaucus*) is a mysterious rodent that is only known from three museum specimens. The last of these was collected in 1956 and the mouse is presumed to be extinct.

Above: The Eastern Chestnut Mouse (*Pseudomys gracilicaudatus*) occurs in "pockets" along the east coast of Queensland and New South Wales. It is most common in heath that is regenerating after burning.

Australian native mice are delicate, soft-furred animals with large ears. These creatures vary in size from a small rat to a tiny mouse. Many are only found in arid areas, while others are only found in specific habitats.

THERE ARE THREE MAIN GROUPS OF NATIVE MICE: the hopping-mice (*Notomys* species); the melomys or "mosaic-tailed" mice (*Melomys* species); and the "false" mice (*Pseudomys* and *Leggadina* species), which are the most numerous.

HOPPING MICE

Most rodents can move with a bounding gait, but some have taken this a stage further and become genuine "hoppers". This type of movement characterises a group of native mice that live in arid and semi-arid parts of Australia.

Hopping-mice avoid the extreme heat of these areas by sheltering in extensive warren systems in small social groups. Their burrows can be more than 1 m below ground and up to 5 m long. Usually, about five individuals will live in one or two adjacent burrow systems.

Right: Hopping-mice obtain all their water needs from their food, which includes seeds, roots, shoots, green plants and small invertebrates.

Conservation Watch

Seven species are Extinct.
Three species are Endangered.
Six species are Vulnerable.

"FALSE MICE"

Some native mice (*Pseudomys* and *Leggadina* species) have been called "false mice" because of their superficial similarity to European mice. However, each species has its own special characteristics and they live everywhere from high alpine scree to dense forest and desert dunes.

Pebble-mound mice are a fascinating group of *Pseudomys*. These small, reddish or fawn-coloured mice build mounds of pebbles up to 9 sq m in area. The mice carry pebbles from the surrounding area in their mouths.

Each mound has one or more active entrances and each entrance has clusters of small pebbles around a large opening. These entrance holes lead into nesting chambers that may extend for several metres underground.

Above: Delicate Mice (*Pseudomys delicatulus*) live in open habitats in soft or sandy soils. They can even be found living in coastal sand dunes.

Above: The Plains Mouse (*Pseudomys australis*) is the largest arid-zone "false" mouse.

"MOSAIC-TAILED" MICE

Melomys, or "mosaic-tailed" mice, have naked tails like typical rats and mice, but the scales are arranged in a mosaic pattern instead of in concentric rows.

Australia has four species of *Melomys* and most are agile climbers that can move swiftly along spindly vines and branches in the tropical and subtropical habitats in which they live. They feed on leaves, seeds, berries, fruit, insects and other arthropods. *Melomys* are active at night and nest in thick vegetation or in trees. Females have four long teats and usually rear two young. The young can remain attached to the teats if the female has to flee the nest.

Left: Melomys are about the size of a small rat, with short ears and light brown to orange-brown fur.

The Dusky Hopping-mouse (*Notomys fuscus*) is now largely confined to the dune fields of the Strzelecki Desert of Central Australia.

One endangered native rodent is the Hastings River Mouse (*Pseudomys oralis*) from the mountain forests of southern Queensland and northern New South Wales.

The Tropical Short-tailed Mouse (*Leggadina lakedownensis*) is a little-known species that can be unexpectedly aggressive when caught.

New Holland Mice (*Pseudomys novaehollandiae*) shelter and breed in burrows systems that may be several metres long.

Dingo
— icon or pest?

Order: Carnivora
Meaning: *caro* — flesh; *vorare* — to devour (devourers of flesh)

The Dingo (Canis lupus dingo) is Australia's wild dog. Although it is the largest carnivorous land mammal in the country, there is debate about whether it is a "true" native animal.

the FACTS!

THE OLDEST DINGO FOSSIL is more than 3000 years old.

ABORIGINAL PEOPLE ADOPTED the Dingo as a companion animal, using it to assist with hunting and for warmth in cold times, but did not domesticate it. Instead, companion Dingoes were taken from the wild and reared by hand, so that they "socialised" with humans.

SOME RESEARCHERS NOW BELIEVE the Dingo is descended from the Indian, or White-footed, Wolf (*Canis lupus pallipes*) and that it is just one of a number of subspecies of the Wolf (*Canis lupus*).

ON THE AUSTRALIAN MAINLAND 80–100 per cent of Dingo populations have crossbred with domestic dogs. One of the last remaining genetically pure populations of the Dingo is found on Fraser Island, Queensland.

IT IS SAID THAT THE TERMS, "two-dog-night" and "three-dog-night" originated with Aboriginal people describing overnight temperatures. Others claim the terms originated with the Native Americans.

ITS ORIGINS ARE UNCERTAIN and there is dispute about whether it is a native animal, or the first in a long line of deliberate introductions by humans.

No-one is really sure who introduced the Dingo to Australia. Aboriginal people had been living in Australia for tens of thousands of years before the ancestral Dingoes arrived about 3000–4000 years ago.

Above: Dingo coat colour can vary from tan to red and even black; however, all colour types have white (or pale) socks and tail tips.

HELP FROM HUMANS

Dingo numbers are believed to be higher now than before European settlement because there is more prey (livestock and feral animals) and more permanent water available.

Although Dingoes are found over much of Australia, not all wild dogs are Dingoes; some are hybrids and others are feral dogs. The distribution of purebred and hybrid Dingoes varies.

Above: The Dingo has erect, pointed ears and a heavier skull and larger teeth than a similar-sized domestic dog.

MARTIN WILLIS

NOT TOO FUSSY

Dingoes are opportunistic predators that eat whatever prey is most available and easily caught. They usually hunt alone or in pairs but will also hunt in packs when pursuing large animals and are most active around dawn and dusk.

Dingoes mainly take mammals, ranging from small dasyurids and rodents, to kangaroos and wallabies, but birds, amphibians, reptiles and insects may also be included in their diet. They will scavenge road-kill and food scraps.

There is no doubt that Dingoes attack livestock, especially calves and lambs, but the damage they inflict on herds and flocks varies. At the same time, Dingoes also prey on feral pigs, goats and rabbits and have been observed killing fox cubs and feral cats.

the FACTS!

WILD DINGOES HOWL and give a short bark when greeting pack members. If they are kept with domestic dogs, they learn to bark.

ALTHOUGH PEOPLE HAVE KEPT DINGOES as domestic dogs, particularly in western areas, Dingoes are not as easily controlled because they tend to retain their wild traits.

Above: Female Dingoes weigh about 12 kg and males up to 15 kg.

Above: Dingoes gradually move around their large home territories by spending a few days in one place and then moving to another.

THE DINGO OR DOG FENCE is a 5320 km barrier fence that was constructed in the 1880s to keep the Dingo out of south-eastern Australia.

DINGOES ARE KNOWN TO CARRY and transmit a number of diseases and parasites, such as distemper and hydatid parasites, which can be passed on to other mammals.

A DINGO HYBRID is often recognisable by broken, patchy or brindled colours.

HOME LIFE

Dingoes live in family groups that defend their territory and sometimes hunt together in packs. Their home range may be up to 8000 ha, but their daily movements take in only a small part of this larger area.

Dingoes mate only once every year (unlike domestic dogs, which breed twice each year), usually between March and June. Dominant pairs mate for life, or as long as they are able to remain dominant.

Above: Litter sizes for Dingoes range from four to six pups, which may be abandoned after a few months, once they are weaned, or may stay with the parents for up to a year if they are in a pack.

DINGO VERSUS THYLACINE

It is thought that the cooperative pack behaviour of Dingoes gave them an important competitive advantage over the more solitary marsupial carnivores, such as the Thylacine (Tasmanian Tiger).

Above: Whales breathe through their blowholes. A flap of skin prevents water entering when they are underwater.

Marine mammals
— sounds of the deep

Order: Cetacea
Meaning: *cetus* — whale (whales)

More than 50 species of marine mammals swim in the tropical, temperate and sub-Antarctic waters off the Australian coast. They include whales, dolphins, seals, sea-lions and Dugongs.

MARINE MAMMALS have all undergone major evolutionary changes in order to survive in their watery environments. Some, like whales, dolphins and Dugongs, cannot survive out of the ocean. Others, like the seals, are efficient hunters in the water, but must still return to land to give birth to their young.

WHALES AND DOLPHINS

Cetaceans (whales and dolphins) range in size from a little over 1 m long all the way up to 30 m long. They are divided into two groups — those with teeth (toothed whales) and those that filter with special sieves in their mouths (baleen whales).

Although, cetaceans look fish-like, they are still warm-blooded air-breathers, so they must come to the surface to breathe. Cetaceans have nostrils called "blowholes", which are located on the top of the head to easily access the air.

Above: The ancestors of cetaceans like this Humpback Whale (*Megaptera novaeangliae*) were terrestrial mammals that lived more than 50 million years ago.

the FACTS!

WHEN WHALES AND DOLPHINS EXHALE, a column of condensation from their blowholes forms and the noise may be heard more than 1 km away.

THE TERM "WHALE" usually refers to the largest of the toothed whales and all of the large baleen whales.

THE TAIL OF A LARGE WHALE is broad and has a clean edge when it is undamaged or the animal is newborn. Scientists use marks on the tail, caused by fighting or attacks by predators, to identify individual whales.

A NEW-BORN BLUE WHALE CALF weighs 2.5 t and in the latter stages of suckling puts on 100 kg in weight a day.

WHALE SONGS consist of a distinct sequence of groans, moans, roars, sighs and high-pitched squeals that may last up to 10 minutes or longer. Baleen whales do not have vocal chords so scientists are still unsure how their songs are produced.

SONG OF THE SEA

Sound is very important to whales and dolphins for hunting, navigating and communicating. Toothed whales and baleen whales use sound quite differently. Toothed whales and dolphins use echolocation for hunting and navigating, whereas baleen whales produce a series of sounds that are frequently termed "songs". It is thought these sounds are used for communication and could also be used for navigation, long-range contact or to warn of threats.

Above: A group of whales is called a "pod". Dolphins are smaller members of the whale family. They also form pods.

Baleen whales
— grand travellers

Order: Cetacea
Meaning: *cetus* — whale (whales)

Baleen whales strain huge mouthfuls of water through the baleen "curtains" in their mouths to catch tiny crustaceans, known as krill, when they feed. Baleen, composed of keratin, looks like thick hair. The whales have long folds of skin or "pleats" running from below the mouth back to the belly, allowing the mouth and throat to expand when taking in water.

AS THE WATER STRAINS OUT through spaces between the baleen, the prey animals are trapped against the bristly curtains and swallowed. These whales eat other marine animals, including small fish, but the shrimp-like Antarctic Krill (*Euphausia superba*) is the most important prey.

Above: A Blue Whale gulps up to 50 t of water each time it opens its mouth to feed.

M CARWARDINE-STILL PICTURES/AUSCAPE

THE BLUE WHALE

The largest living animal is the Blue Whale (*Balaenoptera musculus*), which can reach more than 30 m in length and weigh more than 200 t.

Little is known about Blue Whales. Their breeding grounds are thought to lie somewhere in the deep oceanic waters of the tropical South Pacific, Atlantic and Indian Oceans. Blue Whales are sometimes seen off the coast of southern Australia. There have been strandings in Victoria, South Australia and Western Australia.

HUMPBACK WHALES

Humpback Whales are one of the most active whales and frequently breach, slap their tails and fins on the water surface and engage in vigorous competition for mates when breeding.

Humpback Whales undertake the longest known annual migration of any mammal. Some travel from the Antarctic Peninsula, south of Cape Horn, across the Equator to Columbia and even Mexico.

Below: Humpbacks are heavily built whales and their pectoral fins are up to 5 m long.

GARY BELL/OCEANWIDE IMAGES

the FACTS!

WHALING REDUCED SOUTHERN HEMISPHERE BLUE WHALES from an estimated 225,000 individuals to the current population of less than 2000. In one area of the southern oceans, more than 30,000 Blue Whales were killed in the 1930–1931 season alone.

ALTHOUGH THEY WERE HUNTED almost to extinction, Humpback numbers have shown signs of recovery since the introduction of whaling bans in the 1960s. Populations that breed in Australian waters have almost doubled in the past 10 years.

RIGHT WHALES AND OTHERS

Right whales inhabit the world's southern oceans. During the warmer months of the year Southern Right Whales (*Eubalaena australis*) feed on krill in sub-Antarctic waters, but in winter they migrate northwards to warmer waters for calving, mating or nursing their young before returning south again in spring. Right whales breed in the shallow waters off the southern Australian coast, especiallly in the Great Australian Bight in winter.

The Pygmy Right Whale (*Caperea marginata*) is the smallest of all baleen whales, weighing just 4.5 t, while the Southern Right Whale is more than 10 times its size, at 40–80 t.

Other types of baleen whales include the Minke, Sei and Fin whales. All are found in the Australian waters.

Toothed whales
— deep ocean divers

Order: Cetacea
Meaning: *cetus* — whale (whales)

Unlike baleen whales, which filter food, toothed whales are predators that feed on fish, squid and other marine creatures. The number and shape of their teeth vary according to the species. This group includes sperm whales, beaked whales, Killer Whales, porpoises and dolphins.

the FACTS!

FEMALE SPERM WHALES care for their young as a group. When danger threatens, the entire pod forms a circle or "rosette" with tails out and with the calves protected in the centre.

OIL FROM SPERM WHALES was used to make candles, lamps, soap and perfume. Another valuable substance produced by sperm whales is ambergris, a waxy discharge that may help the whales expel hard objects, such as squid beaks, from their bodies. In earlier times, ambergris was used for perfume and in medical products, but today it has largely been replaced by synthetic products.

BEAKED WHALES are medium-sized cetaceans, ranging from 3 m to 15 m long and weighing about 1–15 t.

SCIENTISTS SUSPECT SPERM WHALES may use a burst of sonar to stun their prey.

BEAKED WHALES feed on deep-water, bottom-dwelling cephalopods, crustaceans and fish, which are caught by "suction-feeding". The whales draw water and prey into their mouths by retracting their tongue and distending their throat. The water is expelled through partly open jaws and the prey swallowed

SPERM WHALES (*Physeter macrocephalus*), are the largest of the toothed whales. They feed deep below the surface, on or near the ocean floor, where they hunt giant squid (*Architeuthis* species) and fish. The whales can dive to depths of around 2.8 km and can stay submerged for more than an hour!

The three species of sperm whale each have enormous "square" heads that hold a waxy liquid substance called "sperm oil", which was much prized by early whalers. Sperm whales occur in deep water off the continental shelf and have been seen in all states. Strandings have been reported in southern Australia, mostly in Tasmania.

Above: Sperm whales occur in all oceans of the world. An adult whale can weigh up to 50 t and even a newborn weighs about 1 t!

BEAKED WHALES

About 20 species of beaked whales have been recorded, but some have never been seen alive and only dead animals, or their skeletons, have been found. Little is known about their biology or life cycles.

Beaked whales are deep ocean divers and can stay submerged for periods of up to 20 or 30 minutes and sometimes as long as 90 minutes, feeding on the ocean floor. Male beaked whales have a short tusk-like tooth on either side of the lower jaw.

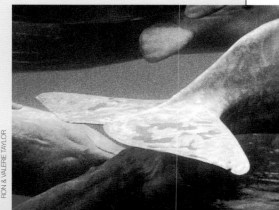

Right: Whales have horizontal tail flukes that move up and down to propel them through the water. Fish have vertical tails that move from side to side.

Orcas & dolphins
— social communicators

Order: Cetacea
Meaning: *cetus* — whale (whales)

Surprising as it seems, ferocious Orcas (Killer Whales) and playful dolphins are closely related members of the same family. Although it is called a "whale", the Orca is actually the largest of all dolphins, one of 20 species of dolphins and porpoises found in Australian waters.

DOLPHINS AND PORPOISES are highly intelligent, social animals that live together in pods. Many species have prominent, beak-like snouts and all have bulging foreheads. Colour varies from plain greys and browns to the striking black and white of the Orcas.

Orcas (*Orcinus orca*) are sometimes called the "wolves of the sea" because they hunt in pods. They are born into a family group and remain there for the rest of their lives. Orcas call extensively to keep in touch with each other and to coordinate their hunting behaviour. They are found almost everywhere throughout the Earth's oceans, but prefer colder waters.

the FACTS!

IN GENERAL, THE WORD "PORPOISE" is used to describe the smallest cetaceans. Porpoises usually have spade-shaped teeth and dolphins have conical or rounded teeth.

DUE TO THE CONSTANT DANGER of predators, dolphins don't sleep; they just nap for about 30 minutes with half their brain still alert.

DOLPHINS USE SONAR to create acoustic pictures of their surroundings, similar to the way bats echolocate. They can produce an extremely high-pitched "whistle" from their blowholes and their sonar takes the form of high-pitched "clicks".

BOTTLENOSE DOLPHINS possess one of the highest ratios of brain size to body mass in the animal world.

D.PARER & E.PARER-COOK/AUSCAPE

Above: Orcas hunt fish, squid, penguins and seals and they have even been known to attack Blue Whales.

LOVABLE DOLPHINS

Dolphins are fast, agile swimmers, well known for their ability to leap out of the water and for "surfing" on waves and near the bows of boats and ships. The Spinner Dolphin (*Stenella longirostris*) will even twist or spin its body as it leaves the water.

Dolphins live in pods of about 15 individuals and communicate with each other using body posture, bubble-blowing, chemical releases, sound, touch and splashing on the water's surface. They can stay submerged for about 15 minutes, swimming to depths of more than 100 m to catch fish, octopus, squid and shrimp.

Left: A typical dolphin grows 2–4 m long and weighs 90–650 kg. The Indo-Pacific Bottlenose Dolphin (*Tursiops aduncus*) is probably the most familiar species.

Conservation Watch

Secure. Local threats: disturbance, poor water quality, damage to seagrass, fishing nets and boat strikes.

Dugong
— seagrass "mermaids"

Order: Sirenia
Meaning: *seiren* — sea nymph (sea nymphs)

Dugongs (Dugong dugon) are one of the few marine mammals that live on plants and, for this reason, they are also known as "sea cows". They graze on seagrass meadows in sheltered coastal waters and, as they feed, whole plants are uprooted, leaving a telltale trail.

the FACTS!

EARLY EXPLORERS and sailors believed that Dugongs and their relatives were mermaids, because of their body shape and the large teats under their flippers.

INDIGENOUS COMMUNITIES throughout northern Australia and the Torres Strait hunted the Dugong for food.

BEN CROPP/AUSCAPE

THE NEAREST LIVING RELATIVES of Dugongs and the related Manatees are elephants.

DUGONGS USE THEIR FRONT FLIPPERS for balance and steering through the water. They never come to land.

RON & VALERIE TAYLOR

DUGONGS ARE LONG-LIVED animals (about 70 years), breeding slowly (once in three to seven years). Females give birth to a single young after 13–15 months. Young Dugongs start feeding on seagrass soon after birth, but will suckle from the mother for up to 18 months.

ALTHOUGH THEY OCCUR IN shallow tropical waters throughout the Indo–Pacific region, most of the world's Dugongs are found in northern Australian waters between Shark Bay in Western Australia and Moreton Bay in Queensland.

A Dugong can reach about 3 m long and weigh up to 400 kg. Despite their size, Dugongs are slow, gentle creatures that propel themselves through the water using their whale-like tail. Unlike cetaceans, Dugongs cannot hold their breath under water for very long and they must surface every few minutes, especially if they are active.

SIGHT AND SOUND

Dugongs have a rounded head, small eyes and a large fleshy snout. Their eyesight is poor, but they have acute hearing to alert them to predators and other threats. They are able to locate and grasp seagrass with the aid of the coarse, sensitive bristles that cover their upper lips.

GARY BELL/OCEANWIDE IMAGES

Above: There is no evidence of large-scale Dugong migration, but some individual animals may travel up to 600 km along the coastline.

Right: Dugongs are easily detected under the water during aerial surveys of their numbers.

JEAN-PAUL FERRERO/AUSCAPE

Seals & sea-lions
— underwater speedsters

Order: Carnivora
Meaning: *caro* — fles; *vorare* — to devour (devourers of flesh)

Two groups of seals inhabit southern Australian waters. The most common are the "eared seals", which include fur-seals and sea-lions. These are often kept in aquariums and zoos. The second group are the "true seals", which breed in Antarctica and are seldom seen near mainland Australia.

EARED SEALS have small flaps of skin over their ear openings. The other main difference between the two groups is that the eared seals can rotate their limbs. On land, they are able to hold themselves upright using their front flippers and, by pulling their hindlimbs under their bodies, they are able to move forwards in an awkward shuffling manner.

True seals are unable to rotate their limbs and so they are less agile on land. They lunge forwards and then wriggle along as best they can for locomotion.

Above: A thick layer of fat insulates seals against the extreme cold of Antarctic waters.

SLEEK HUNTERS

Seals are most at home in the water, where their streamlined "torpedo" shape gives them speed and power. Most seals eat squid, fish and krill, but the Leopard Seal (*Hydrurga leptonyx*) also preys on seabirds, penguins and other seals.

The most common seals in Australian waters are the Australian Sea-lion (*Neophoca cinerea*), New Zealand Fur-seal (*Arctocephalus forsteri*) and Australian Fur-seal (*Arctocephalus pusillus doriferus*).

Left: Australian Sea-lions loafing in the sun on a sandy beach.

the FACTS!

THE AUSTRALIAN SEA-LION is the only species of seal unique to Australia. Their total population size is around 10,000–12,000 individuals.

LIKE WHALES, SEALS WERE ONCE HUNTED EXTENSIVELY. In Australia, hunting began in the late 18th century. The fur-seals were targeted for their skins. Seals are also used for food and oil.

SUBMERGED SEALS close their nostrils and soft palate to prevent the entry of water to the windpipe and gullet when diving.

THE LARGEST BREEDING COLONY of Australian Fur-seals is at Seal Rocks in Victoria, which has an estimated population of 30,000–50,000 animals.

A SEAL'S BLOOD can carry three times more oxygen than human blood.

THE DISTRIBUTION OF LEOPARD SEALS is influenced by the annual expansion and contraction of the pack ice surrounding Antarctica. The highest densities of Leopard Seals are found on broken ice near the edge of the pack ice.

Conservation
— an uncertain future

Australia has some of the world's most unusual and beautiful mammals. It also has the highest extinction rate of native mammals, accounting for one-third of all the mammals that have died out in the world in the past 400 years.

the FACTS!

THE GREATEST THREAT to any animal is habitat destruction, but those that survive are often doomed anyway because of reduced food supply, exposure to the elements, a high risk of predation and, finally, increased competition for the remaining territories.

HOUSE CATS (above) have been in Australia at least since the first European settlers and may have arrived with Dutch shipwrecks in the 17th century. Intentional releases were made in the late 1800s in the hope that cats would control rabbits, rats and mice. Feral cats are now found in most habitats, including offshore islands, but not in the wettest rainforests.

DURING THE 19TH CENTURY, "acclimatisation societies" deliberately tried to replace native species with exotic plants and animals because they were trying to make Australia more like England.

THE CANE TOAD (*Bufo marinus*) is another Australian "ecological disaster". Introduced in 1935 to control insect pests on sugar cane farms, the toad breeds rapidly, is highly poisonous, and competes with native animals for food and shelter. No effective control has ever been found.

THE INTRODUCED EUROPEAN RABBIT (*Oryctolagus cuniculus*) has also been described as an "ecological disaster". The first 24 rabbits were released in 1859 and spread at a rate of about 130 km per year. By 1926, Australia's rabbit population was estimated at 10 billion.

THE "WAVE" OF MAMMAL EXTINCTIONS that followed European settlement of Australia has continued to the present day. A number of species are now in decline and eight species that are already extinct on the mainland have only survived because of their presence on offshore islands.

Our wild animals still face a number of threats, both natural and human-induced. Sometimes these threats are small or localised but, when they are linked to other pressures or to extreme natural conditions, such as cyclones, drought, fires and global warming, the results can be catastrophic.

ALTHOUGH OUR NATIVE ANIMALS are now protected and some past risks, such as hunting, have been mostly removed, many species will still struggle for survival as the 21st century progresses.

The single most serious threat to our native mammals is loss of habitat through land clearing and degradation due to grazing, agriculture, urban development, fires and weeds. When natural habitats are divided or isolated by the pressures of human activities, wild animals are unable to sustain their life cycles and perish.

If competiton and predation by introduced animals and global problems such as pollution and climate change are added to this, the outlook is even more bleak.

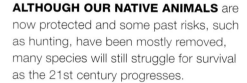

Above: Every year hundreds of thousands of hectares of Australian bushland are cleared for farming and urban growth such as housing development.

Above: Originally imported as domestic food animals, feral goats (*Capra hircus*) and pigs have had a serious impact on Australia's natural environment.

Left: Camels (*Camelus dromedarius*) were imported in the 19th century to provide inland transport. Feral populations impact native vegetation and water supplies that native animals need to survive on.

Saving our
mammals

Before anything can be done to save a threatened species, or to preserve a natural environment, we need to understand individual animals, their behaviour, relationships and life cycles, and their place in the environment.

THE PRESERVATION OF HABITAT is the first and most important step in protecting our native animals. One way to achieve this is to support the expansion and maintenance of Australia's national parks, state forests and other nature reserves. For some species, such as rainforest possums, large reserves containing suitable trees may be all that is needed to ensure the animal's survival. However, for many other animals, particularly those that move around or have special needs, the situation is more complex. In this case, a system of linked reserves and active habitat management, such as controlled burning, can be effective, as can raising public awareness that materialises into help or active participation in programs.

Above: Areas that have a variety of habitats and permanent water will provide homes for many kinds of mammals.

the
FACTS!

NINETEEN SPECIES of mammal have become extinct since European settlement of Australia. Another nine species are extinct on the mainland but survive on offshore islands. Most extinctions have occurred among ground-dwelling mammals from arid and semi-arid parts of inland Australia.

SOME FAUNA RESERVES are owned and managed by non-government organisations.

RECLAIMING LOST GROUND

A number of Australian mammals that became extinct on the mainland survived on nearby islands. They were saved because they were isolated from feral animals that had upset the environmental balance.

Feral animals prey on native wildlife, compete for food and living space, and spread disease. Where feral animals have been controlled or excluded from natural areas on the mainland, it is sometimes possible to re-establish populations of native threatened species.

Captive breeding of native animals is an important part of reclaiming the natural environment.

By protecting and securing the future of our native wildlife, Australians will be able to enjoy them for generations to come.

Right: Habitat conservation is not just a matter of protecting trees. Shelter sites and groundcover must also be preserved to maintain mammal diversity.

Web links & further reading

AUSTRALIAN MAMMALS

ABC animal site — a range of animals including mammals:
www.abc.net.au/schoolstv/animals

Wildsound — Australian Mammal Sound Library:
www.abc.net.au/archives/av/mammals.htm

University of Tasmania, School of Zoology:
www.zoo.utas.edu.au

Australian Mammals:
www.austmus.gov.au/mammals/resources/links.htm

Australian Platypus Conservancy: www.Platypus.asn.au

Marine Species Conservation —
Whale, dolphins and Porposies — Environment Australia:
www.environment.gov.au/coasts/species/cetaceans/index.html

Australian Cetacean Organisations:
www.oceania.org.au/wwwlinks/auorg.html

Queensland Museum: www.qm.qld.gov.au

Mammals of Tasmania — Parks and Wildlife of Tasmania:
www.parks.tas.gov.au/factsheets/wildlife/Mammals.pdf

CONSERVATION

Western Australian Department of Conservation and Land
Management — Nature Base: www.calm.wa.gov.au

Threatened Species and Ecological Communities:
www.environment.gov.au/biodiversity/threatened

World Wildlife Fund — Australia: www.wwf.org.au

Waterfall Springs — captive breeding of the Brush-tailed
Rock-wallaby program: www.waterfallsprings.com.au

FOSSIL MAMMALS

Australia's Lost Kingdoms — Australian Museum site:
www.lostkingdoms.com

Australian Fossil Mammal Sites:
www.environment.gov.au/heritage/worldheritage/sites/fossil

Fossil sites of Australia: www.amonline.net.au/fossil_sites/

Bluff Downs: www.amonline.net.au/fossil_sites/bluff.htm

Lightning Ridge: www.amonline.net.au/fossil_sites/lightning.htm

Murgon: www.amonline.net.au/fossil_sites/murgon.htm

Naracoorte: www.amonline.net.au/fossil_sites/naracoorte.htm

Riversleigh: www.amonline.net.au/fossil_sites/riversleigh.htm

RARE, ENDANGERED AND EXTINCT SPECIES

Biodiversity Unit — Environment Australia —
Threatened species and ecological communities:
www.environment.gov.au/biodiversity/threatened

CSIRO Endangered Species Research:
www.cse.csiro.au/research/aglands/threatenedspecies

Threatened Species of Tasmania —
Tasmanian Parks and Wildlife:
www.dpiwe.tas.gov.au/inter.nsf/ThemeNodes/RLIG-53KUPV

Queensland's Endangered Species — Queensland Museum:
www.qm.qld.gov.au/features/endangered

Queensland's Endangered plants and animals — Queensland
Department of the Environment and Heritage: www.epa.qld.gov.
au/nature_conservation/wildlife/threatened_plants_and_animals

Threatened Species in Victoria — Parks Victoria: www.parkweb.
vic.gov.au/1process_content.cfm?section=26&page=25

New South Wales National Parks and Wildlife Service —
threatened species in New South Wales: www.nationalparks.nsw.
gov.au/npws.nsf/content/threatened+species

Conservation Research — Perth Zoo, Western Australia:
www.perthzoo.wa.gov.au/Conservation--Research

Leadbeater's Possum: www.environment.gov.au/biodiversity/
threatened/publications/recovery/leadbeaters-possum

Thylacine — Australian Museum site:
www.amonline.net.au/thylacine

Thylacine Museum — Images and information on the Thylacine:
www.naturalworlds.org/thylacine

SOCIETIES AND ORGANISATIONS

The Marsupial Society of Australia:
www.marsupialsociety.org

Royal Zoological Society of New South Wales:
www.rzsnsw.org.au

Gilbert's Potoroo Action Group:
www.potoroo.org

Save the Bilby Fund: www.savethebilbyfund.com

WIRES - Wildlife Rescue Organisation:
www.wires.org.au

Native Animal Network Association:
www.nana.asn.au

Glossary

ARBOREAL Living in trees.

CAMOUFLAGE Protective colouration, which blends with background.

CARNIVORE An animal that eats other animals, e.g. the Dingo.

CETACEANS Group of ocean mammals, which includes whales, dolphins and porpoises.

CHLAMYDIA Disease that affects Koalas, one form of which may lead to reproductive tract infection and reduced fertility.

CLASSIFICATION The process of naming and identifying things.

CLOACA One cavity at the end of the digestive tract, which also receives the openings of the urinary and female genital/reproductive system. The cloaca is present in monotremes.

CONVERGENT EVOLUTION Unrelated animals that have similar lifestyles often look similar, even though they are not closely related.

DASYURIDS Group of carnivorous/ insectivorous Australian marsupials, which includes quolls, phascogales, antechinuses, Tasmanian Devil, dunnarts, etc.

DIPROTODONT Having only one functional pair of incisors in the lower jaw. Typical of herbivore dentition.

DIURNAL An animal that is active during the day.

ECHOLOCATION Sensing objects by sending out sounds then analysing the echoes reflected after they impact.

EMBRYO Animal in developmental stage between conception and birth.

EXTINCT When an animal, plant, or other living organism ceases to exist.

FERAL Having reverted to a wild state.

GENUS The classification of a group of organisms that share many characteristics; a genus may contain one or more species.

GESTATION Time between conception and birth.

HABITAT Place where a particular animal or plant lives or grows. Area where a species is able to survive.

HERBIVORE Animal that eats plants.

HIBERNATION Period of prolonged inactivity and lowered metabolism brought about by cold weather.

INCUBATE Keep eggs warm so they develop and hatch.

INSECTIVORE Animals which eat mainly insects, e.g. dunnart.

INVERTEBRATE An animal without a backbone.

LINNEAN SYSTEM Plant and animal classification developed by Carl von Linnaeus in the 18th century.

MACROPODS Group of herbivorous Australian marsupials with strong hindlegs, which includes kangaroos and wallabies.

METABOLISM Chemical processes, which sustain life.

MICRO-ORGANISM Minute living creatures such as bacteria and protozoa. Their activity in the digestive system breaks down plant cellulose so the body can use the products.

MONOTREME A mammal that lays eggs and possesses a cloaca. It feeds its young on milk but lacks nipples.

NATIVE An animal or plant species belonging to the land, as distinguished from foreign species.

NOCTURNAL Active at night.

OMNIVORE Animal that eats plants and animals.

PLACENTA Vascular sac connecting the circulatory system of unborn infant to that of its mother. The placenta is expelled from the uterus after birth. Monotremes do not develop placentas.

PLACENTAL MAMMALS Mammals whose young, through the presence of a placenta, can remain within the mother's body until their development is complete.

POLYPROTONDONT Having more than one pair of lower incisor teeth. Typical of carnivores like dasyuroids.

PREDATOR Animal that hunts and eats animals.

PREHENSILE Able to grip.

PRIMATES Group of mammals, which includes tarsiers, monkeys, apes and humans.

RODENTS Group of gnawing animals, including mice and rats.

SCAVENGER Animals that eat dead animals.

SILICA A very hard chemical compound. Sand is an example.

SPECIES A group of organisms that can breed to produce fertile offspring with similar characteristics.

TAXONOMY The science of classifying (describing and naming) plants and animals.

TERRESTRIAL Living on land.

TERRITORIAL Related to the defence of a territory.

TERRITORY Area occupied and defended by an individual or group.

TORPOR State of inactivity, usually brought about by cold. An animal's metabolic rate slows down and it uses less food reserves.

TOXIC Poisonous.

TRAGUS Fleshy flap on the front of the external ear; in microbats the tragus assists with echolocation.

VERTEBRATES Animals with backbones. Includes fish, amphibians, reptiles, birds, mammals.

WOODLAND Area sparsely covered with trees.

Index